# Witness to Change
## A Record of the Industrial Revolution

# Witness to Change
## A Record of the Industrial Revolution

The Elton Collection
at the
Ironbridge Gorge Museum

## MICHAEL A. VANNS

# Contents

## Acknowledgements

The author would like to thank the following individuals who supported this project: at conception, Ruth Denison, Glen Lawes and Peter Waller; at creation, David de Haan and John Powell; at the photography stage, Joanne Smith and David Houlston.
The author drew heavily on a number of published accounts of the Industrial Revolution, and an unpublished thesis, 'The Contribution of Sir Arthur Elton to Documentary Film Production in Britain' by Paul Collins (presented for the degree of Master of Social Science, Institute of Industrial Archaeology, December 1986), for which he is grateful.

Ironbridge Gorge Museum Trust, Coach Road, Coalbrookdale, Telford, Shropshire TF8 7DQ

Tel: 01952 433522
Web: www.ironbridge.org.uk

First published 2003

ISBN 0 7110 2953 9

Published by Ian Allan Publishing

an imprint of Ian Allan Publishing Ltd, Hersham, Surrey KT12 4RG.

Printed by Ian Allan Printing Ltd, Hersham, Surrey KT12 4RG.

Code 0306/A

Front cover:
The Atmospheric Railway at Dawlish, South Devon Railway
watercolour, March-September 1848
Nicholas Condy (1793-1857)
AE185.49

The 'Railway Age' spawned many fine engineers, and I.K. Brunel was probably the greatest. His work was always based on sound principles, but very often, as with atmospheric traction in place of steam locomotives, the technology of his day could not match his vision.

Back cover:
Top left:
Main Aisle of the Crystal Palace, Great Exhibition, 1851
chromolithograph from 'Dickinson's comprehensive picture of the Great Exhibition of 1851'.
J. Nash, L. Haghe, J. Roberts
AE185.5284

Top right:
Parys Mine
watercolour
Francois Louis Thomas Francia (1772-1839)
AE185.161

Bottom left:
Central tower of the Britannia Tubular Railway Bridge
tinted lithograph (proof before letters)
George Hawkins (1810-52)
AE185.181

Inset:
Bone china mug, with hand-painted view of the Iron Bridge
John Rose Works, Coalport, Shropshire
1820s
AE185.1806

Title page:
Belshazzar's Feast
mezzotint, hand-coloured, 1835
(after) John Martin (1789–1854)
AE185.824

Francis Klingender, in his 1947 book Art and the Industrial Revolution, drew attention to the link between John Martin's vast apocalyptic oil paintings and industry. In the subject matter of this painting, Martin seems to be making a comparison between an ancient civilisation in the throes of self-destruction and his contemporary environment. The overbearing architecture would have reminded viewers of factories, aqueducts and tunnels of their own age.

# Witness to Change
## A Record of the Industrial Revolution

The Elton Collection
at the
Ironbridge Gorge Museum

MICHAEL A. VANNS

# Contents

## Acknowledgements

The author would like to thank the following individuals who supported this project: at conception, Ruth Denison, Glen Lawes and Peter Waller; at creation, David de Haan and John Powell; at the photography stage, Joanne Smith and David Houlston.
The author drew heavily on a number of published accounts of the Industrial Revolution, and an unpublished thesis, 'The Contribution of Sir Arthur Elton to Documentary Film Production in Britain' by Paul Collins (presented for the degree of Master of Social Science, Institute of Industrial Archaeology, December 1986), for which he is grateful.

Ironbridge Gorge Museum Trust, Coach Road, Coalbrookdale, Telford, Shropshire TF8 7DQ

Tel: 01952 433522
Web: www.ironbridge.org.uk

First published 2003

ISBN 0 7110 2953 9

Published by Ian Allan Publishing

an imprint of Ian Allan Publishing Ltd, Hersham, Surrey KT12 4RG.

Printed by Ian Allan Printing Ltd, Hersham, Surrey KT12 4RG.

Code 0306/A

Front cover:
The Atmospheric Railway at Dawlish, South Devon Railway
watercolour, March-September 1848
Nicholas Condy (1793-1857)
AE185.49

The 'Railway Age' spawned many fine engineers, and I.K. Brunel was probably the greatest. His work was always based on sound principles, but very often, as with atmospheric traction in place of steam locomotives, the technology of his day could not match his vision.

Back cover:
Top left:
Main Aisle of the Crystal Palace, Great Exhibition, 1851
chromolithograph from 'Dickinson's comprehensive picture of the Great Exhibition of 1851'.
J. Nash, L. Haghe, J. Roberts
AE185.5284

Top right:
Parys Mine
watercolour
Francois Louis Thomas Francia (1772-1839)
AE185.161

Bottom left:
Central tower of the Britannia Tubular Railway Bridge
tinted lithograph (proof before letters)
George Hawkins (1810-52)
AE185.181

Inset:
Bone china mug, with hand-painted view
of the Iron Bridge
John Rose Works, Coalport, Shropshire
1820s
AE185.1806

Title page:
Belshazzar's Feast
mezzotint, hand-coloured, 1835
(after) John Martin (1789–1854)
AE185.824

Francis Klingender, in his 1947 book Art and the Industrial Revolution, drew attention to the link between John Martin's vast apocalyptic oil paintings and industry. In the subject matter of this painting, Martin seems to be making a comparison between an ancient civilisation in the throes of self-destruction and his contemporary environment. The overbearing architecture would have reminded viewers of factories, aqueducts and tunnels of their own age.

# Foreword by Sir Neil Cossons

**Sir Neil Cossons was the first Director of the Ironbridge Gorge Museum — from 1971 to 1983 — and deeply involved in the fate of the Elton Collection after Sir Arthur Elton's death.**

I had known Arthur Elton from the mid-1960s when Curator of Technology at Bristol City Museum, seen his extraordinary collection at Clevedon Court, and come to regard him as both hero and very dear friend. The number of people who in *Who's Who* list 'industrial archaeology' among their recreations is very, very, few. Arthur was I believe the first. My respect was overwhelming.

I already had a copy of his *British Railways* first published by Collins in 1945 and of course was rapturous when the new and enlarged edition of Francis Klingender's *Art and the Industrial Revolution*, which he edited, appeared in 1968. Both books drew extensively on his outstanding collection. So, when Arthur died, with uncharacteristic tidiness, on 1 January 1973, it was a shock to all who knew and loved him, not least because his unique combination of immense knowledge, spirited collecting, and great charm and humanity, had gone from our lives. His death was also to raise questions of the future of the collection.

It soon became apparent that duties on the estate were going to present a problem and so the collection was offered in lieu, eventually to be accepted by the Treasury at an even then rather modest valuation of — I think — £220,000. With the collection then in the hands of the nation, the nation had to decide what to do with it. Various institutions started to express interest. The Science Museum in South Kensington was one and there were a number of university libraries, including Bristol and Manchester. And, in Ironbridge we saw the synergy of the origins of industrialisation, which the Museum sought to articulate, and the collection that was such a powerful visual expression of its wider inferences, as not just alluring but irresistible.

As the contest began to warm up, Arthur's widow Margaret Ann became, with more than a little enthusiasm on her part, the centre of attention. Paying court at Clevedon Court was clearly going to be essential. She had very strong views, expressed with great passion and rather less prudence, and often at very great length, to anybody who was prepared to listen. As her daughter Julia later reminded me, before she had married Arthur, Margaret Ann Bjornson had been born and brought up in the Icelandic community of Winnipeg. She had, as she put it, 'four Icelandic grandparents'. She was a devoted and well-practised connoisseur of the saga.

As the ante was raised it soon became obvious that some of the competitors were not as committed to doing the collection justice as were others. Crucially, none of them could put it on immediate display. The larger the institution, the less it could offer, the collection representing incremental gain rather than elemental transformation. But to Ironbridge it meant everything. The Trustees of the Museum, under the chairmanship of Bruce Ball, were unequivocal in their enthusiasm. So too was Telford Development Corporation, whose General Manager Emyr Thomas (who was also Honorary Secretary of the Museum and one of its founding fathers) and his Chairman, Lord Northfield, enabled us to substantiate our bid. Sir Arthur Drew, then Chairman of the Museums & Galleries Commission, was a great supporter of the burgeoning new breed of independent museums springing up across the country. He was an Ironbridge enthusiast. And, so were Arthur's daughter, Julia, and the distinguished antiquarian bookseller Ben Weinreb.

But despite this galaxy of support Margaret Ann's view was critical, not least because she broadcast it widely and gave no quarter to those of whom she disapproved. I became an expert listener. Typically, she would telephone at a few minutes before midnight. I sat on my hall floor in Ironbridge and made occasional monosyllabic sounds of acquiescence. Intervention was pointless and unnecessary; agreement was everything. During the 1960s some philistine had covered the floor, a glorious pattern of geometric Jackfield tiles, with a black and white chequerboard of thermoplastic. Listening to Margaret Ann, I sat

with pallet knife in one hand and phone in the other. As the weeks passed I worked my way systematically across the hall, lifting plastic tiles, fragment by fragment, as I listened to declamatory assertions about the University of Manchester Institute of Science & Technology or the Science Museum in London. 'I will not let these people get their hands on Arthur's collection' was a frequent refrain. An hour or so later the phone would go dead; she always signed off in mid-sentence. Despite all this I came to like Margaret Ann enormously, not least for her unambiguous luminosity of expression and droll, if anguished, humour.

The Ironbridge Gorge Museum was allocated the Elton Collection. Within a year it was on display in a purpose-built gallery, opened with great eloquence by Kingman Brewster, the American Ambassador, on 21 April 1979. The Museum appointed a curator, David de Haan, who, with his close colleagues John Powell and Michael Vanns, care for the collection to this day. There is no question in my mind that it has fared better in the hands of Ironbridge than would have been the case anywhere else. It is widely consulted and well published. It has retained its identity and in so doing kept alive something of the spirit and devotion of its creator, Sir Arthur Elton. Few museums, if any, could look back on 25 years of curatorship with a greater sense of achievement or satisfaction.

*Sir Neil Cossons*
*Shropshire*

Above:
The Museum of Iron (right), and the Long Warehouse (left) in Coalbrookdale. The latter houses the Ironbridge Institute, the Museum's Library and Archive embracing The Elton Collection.

Right:
Top floor of the Coach House Gallery which was the venue for all Elton exhibitions between 1979 and 1983.

# Preface by Julia Elton

On a sunny May morning in 1976 a Treasury official, four tea-chests and a large roll of bubble-wrap arrived together at the front door of Clevedon Court, my family home, where I and two young colleagues were waiting to pack the Elton Collection, which had just been accepted by the Government in lieu of death duties. However, four tea-chests were wholly inadequate to contain 4,000 books, let alone pictures and ephemera, even supposing anyone could carry them when full, so we spent the rest of that day looking for packaging suppliers in Bristol, eventually buying a large number of rectangular cardboard boxes, originally intended to carry a few dozen egg cartons each. I had prepared a catalogue under the eagle eye of the bookseller, Ben Weinreb, who had negotiated the passing over of the collection to the Government. Each book, picture and object had to be checked off against this catalogue, all seven volumes of it. This was difficult for the Treasury man, who was more accustomed to dealing with one or two items at a time and was thrown by such copious and varied quantities of stuff. As time passed, the weather of that boiling summer got hotter and tempers frayed. The Treasury man became grumpy as his role was reduced to fetching endless cold drinks for us harried packers who had to sort, size and wrap everything and then carry the full boxes out into the Screens Passage, while my mother drifted in and out of the Great Hall clutching a large whisky with the tears pouring down her face. After a week or so of unremitting hard physical labour, the collection was finally packed and the house felt stripped bare.

My father was an intensely visual man who combined a distinguished career as a documentary film maker with a passion for the history of technology. Consequently, I grew up surrounded by innumerable images of trains, flaring industrial scenes, iron bridges and masonry viaducts striding across the landscape. They invaded all corners of the house, including the nursery, where Joseph Nash's picture of the closing of the Great Exhibition hung,

Closing of The Great Exhibition, 15 October 1851
watercolour
Joseph Nash (1808-78)
AE185.90

Spirit Flask
Stoneware
Fulham Pottery, c1850
AE185.1821

7

possibly because my father thought its soft pink tints suitable for small girls but mostly because wall space was far too precious to be given over to Peter Rabbit, though he did resist the urging of his great friend, Jean Gimpel, to consign the ancestors to the attic and take over the soaring walls of the Great Hall. As befitted a West Country house, the main staircase was hung with pictures of Brunel's Great Western Railway starting at the bottom with Frith's preliminary sketch for the painting of Paddington Station (see p53) and arriving at the top in Cornwall with the watercolour of Gover Viaduct (see p103), while mezzotint portraits of what seemed to us bewhiskered and steamy old gentlemen paraded down the passages. Books overflowed in every room and every mantelpiece bore a mass of weird and wonderful objects in glass, pottery, brass or papier-mâché, commemorating bridges or railways or water wheels. So it was a bad moment when everything disappeared down the drive in a removal van.

After a fierce debate about its future, the collection was assigned to the young Ironbridge Gorge Museum and our carefully packed egg boxes arrived there in 1978. Twenty-five years on, Michael Vanns' book makes it clear beyond a shadow of doubt that Ironbridge has been the best possible home for the collection. He shows the depth of understanding brought to the collection by the specially appointed curatorial team, led by the highly knowledgeable David de Haan, which has enabled it to be used creatively in a way that my father would have appreciated, and even envied, to interpret for an increasingly interested public the momentous changes wrought in Britain by the Industrial Revolution. Because of the Museum's generous lending policy many of the pictures, notably the banquet in the Thames Tunnel, have become widely known. Michael celebrates my father's great talents as a collector and film-maker, perceptively describing how he welded the various parts of the collection into a seamless whole. Although I still miss many of the pictures and objects, I was lucky to have played a part in such an outstandingly happy success story and to this day, every time David de Haan and I meet, we murmur 'egg-boxes' to each other.

*Julia Elton*
London

# Introduction

It is 25 years since the Elton Collection was allocated to the Ironbridge Gorge Museum Trust, and 30 years since the death of the man who assembled it, Sir Arthur Elton (1906–73). This book is a celebration of those two anniversaries and has been made possible with a grant from Resource, The Council for Museums, Archives & Libraries, as part of that organisation's Designation Challenge Fund award of 2000. The Elton Collection is unique and the finest of its type. Put together during a lifetime of careful acquisition by Sir Arthur Elton, it contains nearly 200 paintings and drawings, over 650 individual prints, a library of over 4,000 books and pamphlets, approximately 800 photographic postcards as well as 200 miscellaneous items embracing pottery,

medallions and other pieces of ephemera, all concerned with the industrial and transport revolutions which took place in Great Britain during the 18th and 19th centuries. There is a certain amount of foreign subject matter [1 and 2], but the strength of the collection lies in the work of contemporary artists, print-makers, writers, publishers and other craftsmen working in this country.

This author has been associated with the collection since October 1978, when he joined the staff at Ironbridge to work as Documentation Assistant for the newly appointed Curator of the Elton Collection, David de Haan MSc, DIC, FMA. Completing the new Elton team and charged

[1]
Tokyo Takanawa Tourist Attraction
wood block engraving, c1890
AE185.444

This extraordinary print includes a representation of the first steam locomotives in Japan. The artist, more used to traditional iconography, has had some difficulty representing the engine. Perhaps he never actually saw it for himself?

9

with cataloguing the books and pamphlets, was professional librarian Marilyn Soden. I can well remember how exciting it was unpacking the collection and watching the paintings [3], drawings and prints emerge from the storage crates, whilst the books went on the shelves. Within weeks we were preparing the first exhibition, ordering the new frames, cutting the mounts from acid-free board, writing the labels and assembling the catalogue. By the New Year the new Elton gallery was almost finished, and I shall never forget having to start hanging the pictures on the first floor of the Coach House Gallery as the last paviours were still being laid on the ground floor. It was an exciting time.

In 1978 the Ironbridge Gorge Museum Trust was only 10 years old. It was one of a new breed of independent museums focusing on Britain's industrial heritage, whilst at the same time challenging established museum display techniques by presenting both the products and processes of the past in interesting and engaging ways. The 18th-century developments in iron-making in and around Ironbridge and Coalbrookdale were crucial factors in the industrialisation of Great Britain [4] and the acquisition of the Elton Collection, containing as it did evidence of the other essential ingredients of the Industrial Revolution, allowed the Museum to put its own story into the broader picture. The collection provided the Museum Trust with a resource of national importance, which supported its aspirations to become a centre for the study of industrial archaeology.

Twenty-five years later, at the beginning of the 21st century, in a post-industrial society, the Elton Collection is arguably more important than it was when first allocated to Ironbridge. Then, most people's understanding of the past was through personal experience and text-book history. The Ironbridge Gorge Museum had yet to put people into Victorian costume as part of its interpretation strategy, and there were no historical re-enactments of any significance. History programmes on

**[4]**
A View of the Upper Works
at Coalbrookdale
engraving, hand-coloured, 1758
François Vivares (1709–80)
after Thomas Smith (d 1767)
and George Perry (1719–71)
AE185.769

This is the earliest known view
of the Coalbrookdale ironworks,
with the blast furnace where
Abraham Darby I carried out
his successful coke smelting
experiments in 1709, behind
the man leaning on the fence.
To the right heaps of coal
are being coked and in the
foreground a team of six horses
is shown pulling a cast-iron
Newcomen steam engine
cylinder made at the works.

television were few and far between and history was certainly not living in the 1970s. Since then people's awareness of 'heritage' has increased enormously. At weekends hundreds of people all over the country drive steam engines or dress up as Roman soldiers, or re-fight Civil War battles. Homes are redecorated in every conceivable historical style, whilst architectural salvage and antiques fairs have become big business. The visual perception of the past is greater now than it ever has been and where there are no contemporary images, the reconstruction artist, the computer animator, provides them. History is understood and perceived today more through vision than the written word. Traditional historians have always been able to express opinions and offer alternative interpretations, but with re-enactments, and 'living' museums, there is less room for conjecture. And that is why the content of the Elton Collection is so valuable. What it reveals are

contemporaries' views of their own time, their own period of history. Those images and written texts give us an insight into how the people at the time perceived their world. They are eye witnesses. The objects are not without bias. Subject matter and presentation were bound by the artistic and literary conventions of the day, and there were, obviously, commercial considerations for those who produced prints, books and commemorative items for sale. But despite this, the material must inevitably bring us closer to the period being recorded, closer than any re-enactment, museum reconstruction or historical interpretation. The strength of the Elton Collection is that it provides a first-hand view of an important watershed in history. The whole collection is a witness to one of the most momentous periods of change in British society. The images, the texts and the ephemera provide a record of a revolution — a record of the Industrial Revolution.

# 1. Creation of the Collection

The Elton Collection is the result of one man's passion for collecting contemporary images and accounts of a period in British history now commonly known as the Industrial Revolution [5]. This subject has been written about extensively and, although relevant historical information is used in Chapter Five as the framework for an appreciation of the collection, it is not the intention here to retell the complete story, nor has an attempt been made to present a fresh interpretation of the period. It is sufficient to relate that this particular revolution did not start with an uprising on a specific day, but developed gradually until by the middle of the 18th century the signs of irreversible change could be clearly discerned all over the country. By then most of the elements that were to transform the British landscape, its society and, ultimately, the world economy were in place. Only the 'railway age' was another generation away and when that came, it could be argued, it conveniently marked the end of the revolution [6]. By 1851, the year of the Great Exhibition, Britain had been turned from an agrarian into an industrialised society. Our life experiences at the beginning of the 21st century have much more in common with the 1850s than the emerging industrial society of a century earlier.

Almost exactly 200 years after the first effects of the Industrial Revolution had been felt, Britain was once again entering a period of economic and social transition following the great catastrophe of World War 2. The next 50 years then witnessed changes as fundamental as those of the period 1750–1850, as the economy moved from its reliance on coal and heavy industry to oil and service industries, and society turned its back on its inherited Victorian legacy. Large-scale redevelopment became a reality for many urban centres, whilst towns that had remained largely unaltered since the Victorian period were changed piecemeal to meet the demands of the motor car. In the 1960s, Britain had firmly entered into the brave new world of modernity.

The changed priorities of postwar Britain are crucial to an understanding of the Elton Collection. The keyword in almost all aspects of society after the war was 'modernisation'. 'Old-fashioned' became a derogatory term.

People were no longer prepared to live as their parents had, surrounded by the paraphernalia of a 'bygone' age. The new generation wanted new things, new music, new fashions, new architecture, new life-styles, and when these went out of vogue, it had no compunction in throwing them away. Old things were to be confined to museums, and not allowed to interfere with everyday life. Not everyone agreed with this, of course, and in his February 1951 review of a new book by Christian Barman, *An Introduction to Railway Architecture*, Sir Arthur Elton made his feelings clear:

'Today ... museums lick their chops over some horror of a Jacobean chair. But any advertising cad can daub a poster over some 19th-century railway masterpiece, and many an uninformed railway official bashes a hole in some delicate façade, or turns it into an improvised bill board ... The solid well-proportioned façade of Worcester, Shrub Hill, has been gashed and mutilated for no apparent reason. A piece of excrement, in the form of a kiosk, has been deposited in the middle of Hardwick's Great Hall at Euston ...'

Sadly, the mutilations and the disregard for the recent past continued. The addition of that kiosk must have seemed a small price to pay when the whole of Euston station was demolished 10 years later [7 and 8].

As the legacy of the Industrial Revolution and the Victorian era became more and more unfashionable, as industrial monuments and landscapes began to disappear, the preservation movement strengthened and Elton's collection grew. There is little doubt that a major driving force behind his desire to collect was the need to preserve and make sense of a period he felt was being sacrificed, unrecorded, in the name of progress. In 1958 he wrote: 'Alas, I cannot collect full-scale locomotives myself ... I have to be content with what I can get into the house.'

By current criteria, his collection is not unusual, but at the time he was putting it together, it would have been seen by other collectors as eccentric. Until comparatively recently there was a definite hierarchy to artefacts from the past. Classification depended on material, maker,

PAINTED BY H. ALKEN. PUBLISHED NOVEMBER 1ST 1852, BY MESS. FORES, 41, PICCADILLY, LONDON. ENGRAVED BY J. HARRIS.

PAINTED BY H. ALKEN. PUBLISHED NOVEMBER 1ST 1852, BY MESS. FORES, 41, PICCADILLY, LONDON. ENGRAVED BY J. HARRIS.

THE DRIVER OF THE MAIL 1852.

THE DRIVER OF THE MAIL 1832.

14

[5] opposite
Fores's Contrasts —
The Driver of the Mail
1832: The Driver of the
Mail 1852
aquatints, hand-coloured
J. Harris after H. Alken
AE185.634

The term 'Industrial Revolution' probably
dates from the 1830s, by which time
contemporary observers were well aware
that their society had undergone radical
change in the last 100 years. Fores was
one of those who tried to illustrate the
changes, and he chose to contrast what
were, for the years 1832 and 1852, the
fastest means of land transport. The
resultant print speaks for itself.

[6]
St James Bridge and
Railway Station, Bath
wash drawing
John Cooke Bourne
(1814–96)
AE185.8

The 'Railway Age' produced some fine
monuments, and this was one. Elton
was fortunate in being able to acquire
this preliminary 'sketch' for just one of
the lithographic plates that appeared in
'The History & Description of the Great
Western Railway', published by David
Bogue in 1846.

[7]
Euston Station, Grand Entrance
engraving
A. Ashley after J. F. Burrell
published in The British
Gazetteer
AE185.683

[8]  opposite
Euston Station from Six
Coloured Views on the London
& Birmingham Railway
aquatint, hand-coloured
J. Harris after Thomas Talbot
Bury (1811–77)
published by Ackermann & Co,
18 September 1837
AE185.4158

Parts of the original train shed at
Euston station, designed by Charles
Fox of the firm Fox Henderson which
cast all the iron for the Great Exhibition
of 1851, survived until 1961.

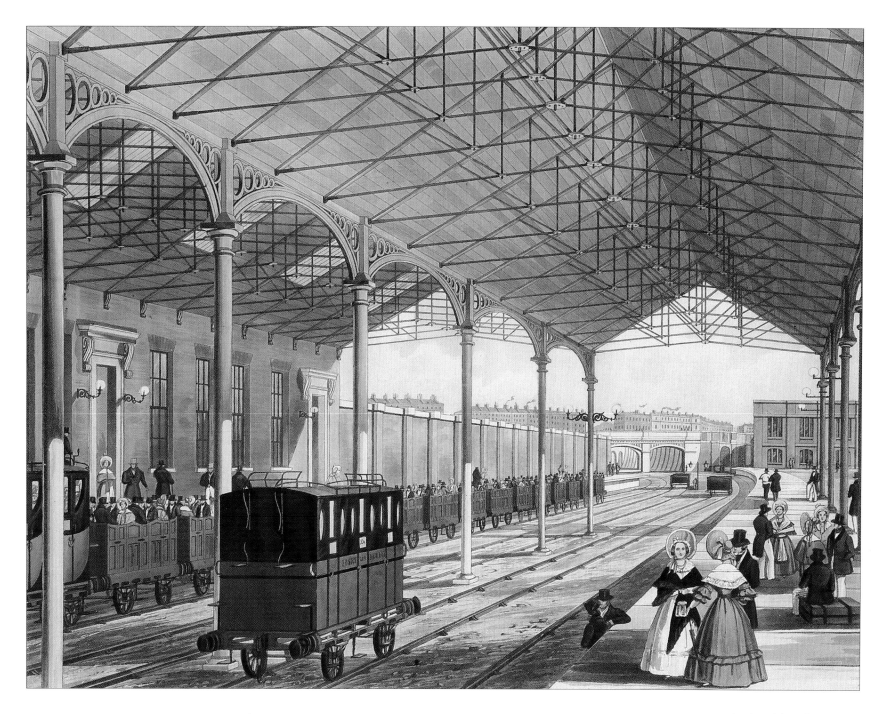

artistic style, cultural origin, and, in particular, monetary value. The boundary between antiques and 'bric-a-brac' was one of value. Quality and taste came at a price. Consequently, collectors of works of fine art would have readily dismissed the Elton Collection. Collectors of prints and drawings would have been confused that it also encompassed contemporary books, pieces of pottery and other miscellaneous ephemera. The curators of the national museums until comparatively recently would also have had difficulty appreciating the collection, still preoccupied as they were with fine objects rather than items of social or working-class history **[9]**.

These distinctions did not worry Elton. He was more interested in the subject matter of his material than its physical and financial attributes: 'I'm an unfashionable collector. My catalogue gives the name of the place followed by the artist ... I'm tired of masterpieces. I look at pictures in a literary way, very nearly as manuscript.' It is not surprising, therefore, that in an article written by him for *The Listener* in February 1958 — 'On Collecting Railwayana' — he focused more attention on his books than his railway prints. Not being a traditional art collector, he did not collect prints, drawings and paintings purely as display items. All the material in his collection was there to be 'read'; it had been brought together as a means of better understanding a particular period of British history: '... my collection ... is becoming the history of how people looked at and thought about the railways and canals and bridges and factories that transformed the face of our country.' This same rationale was evident in his career. He was a documentary film-maker who used images to reinforce facts. He was not a conceptual artist, but a craftsman making useful objects.

This comparison between documentary films and the Elton Collection also throws light on another aspect of the latter. The collection contains almost no items made by the men and women who were the subjects of its books and pictorial material. All the material is at least one step removed from its subject matter, having been filtered through the minds and eyes of its authors and artists. The documentary films of Elton's era were the same because their content was interpreted by director, cameraman and ultimately editor. Although his film *Housing Problems* (1935) was one of the first documentary films in which the subjects, the people, talked to the camera directly, the finished film, none the less, was not of their making. The people were merely the subject. Likewise, the Elton Collection does not have any examples of what became known in the 1970s and 1980s as 'naïve art' or folk art, pictures done by working people with first-hand experience of their

[9]
Norfolk Railway Guard
oil on canvas, 1854
J. Mott
AE185.47

Victorian railways were run like military organisations, with rules, regulations, discipline, hierarchy of personnel and uniforms. Many staff thrived on the security and order this brought to their working lives.

**[10]**
Windsor Station and Castle
wash drawing, c1850
AE185.13

This strange work illustrates
very clearly that although
traditional elements of painting
and drawing objects such as
buildings could be rendered
quite competently, if artists were
not trained in technical drawing,
they could struggle to depict
machinery accurately.

chosen subject but absolutely no artistic training **[10]**. Elton's nearest example of this was his copy of the James Sharples (1825–92) print, 'The Forge' (see p136), produced by a man who worked in the environment depicted in the print and who was, therefore, genuinely the subject of his own work. However, even if an art historian did not have this knowledge, he would never classify Sharples' work as 'naïve art', because it is so clearly and firmly within the accepted tradition of professional British print-making.

Naturally, given the limits of one man's lifespan, the contents of the Elton Collection are also the result of what items were available at the time Elton was interested and had the money to collect them. The collection is not a comprehensive record of Britain's industrial past. Neither is it completely objective. Like all the best collections of individuals when compared with those of publicly accountable archives, museums or art galleries, it is a subjective accumulation of material. It is always intriguing to speculate what positive discrimination a

*Plate III.*

DUBLIN AND KINGSTOWN RAILWAY.

*The Tunnel from the Excavation, looking towards Dublin.*

Dublin, Published by W.F.Wakeman, 9 D'Olier Street, October 1834.

collector exercises when adding to a themed collection. What items were rejected on grounds of content, or quality of image, or condition, or even price? What items would have been acquired if the collector had known of their existence? By contrast, what items did the collector want to purchase but did not have the opportunity?

Because Elton was one of the first to accumulate a collection devoted to industry and transport he was presented simultaneously with both a great opportunity and a handicap. Initially, the items he acquired were of little monetary value as few other collectors were interested in the material. This was an advantage. But it was at the same time a handicap because items of little value can be destroyed with an easier conscience and dealers are less likely to stock the material if there is insufficient demand and return on their initial investment. Having said

that, it is remarkable what did make it into the collection. That was down to Elton's persistence and, as is true of most habitual collectors, the relationships he built up over the years with various dealers. He purchased his 13-plate copy of T. T. Bury's *Liverpool & Manchester Railway* in Amsterdam, and Andrew Nichol's *Five Views of the Dublin & Kingstown Railway* from a dealer in New York who in turn had acquired it in Cologne [11]. During World War 2, the Phillimore Collection came up for auction at Sotheby's, in 1942 and 1943, and Elton successfully bid for a number of items [12].

Obviously, as well as reflecting the perceptions and purchase opportunities of one man, the Elton Collection is nevertheless a record of what other men, the artists, the pamphleteers, the authors, the print-makers, considered was worthy of attention in their restless age. There

[12]
Canterbury from the Railway
lithograph, hand-coloured,
1842
AE185.178

This was one of a number of prints that Elton purchased from the Phillimore Collection. It shows the Canterbury & Whitstable Railway, which opened on 3 May 1830, just four months before the far more influential Liverpool & Manchester Railway (L&MR). Both lines were engineered by George Stephenson, but the L&MR became the template for modern railways.

were new commercial opportunities in producing views of ironworks **[13]**, coalmines **[14]**, bridges, viaducts **[15]** and scenes on the Liverpool & Manchester Railway **[16]**, or bone china with depictions of early railways on them, or glass goblets engraved with images of the Sunderland Bridge (see Chapter Four). And although the individual writers and publishers, artists and print-makers, potters and other craftsmen would have been unaware of it, their output, brought together in the Elton Collection, gives us a unique insight into how the Industrial Revolution affected the nation's psyche. The humorous late 1820s etching, 'The March of Intellect', for example, is a sarcastic antidote to the prevalent view at the time that there was no limit to what man could achieve by harnessing the powers of science and machine — the Grand Vacuum

Tube Company forms a direct connection with Bengal, a suspension bridge links Britain to Cape Town, and a bat-shaped balloon is capable of transporting convicts to New South Wales **[17]**. The print has the same authority as a present-day political cartoon. The dressing table trinket holder made of silver gilt and pieces of nautilus shells and fashioned in the shape of a railway locomotive is a three-dimensional commentary on just how significant to all levels of society was the Railway Mania of the 1840s **[18]**. The child's 'New Railway Game, or Tour Through England' was a preparation for life in the world's most industrialised country.

As a whole, with all its eclectic content, the Elton Collection evokes a heroic view of the industrial and transport revolutions. If it has a

[15]
Chirk Viaduct
lithograph, hand-coloured
George Hawkins (1810–52)
after George Pickering
(1794-1857)
published by T. Catherall,
Chester
AE185.291

Both the Llangollen Canal and
the Shrewsbury & Chester
Railway had to cross the valley
of the River Ceiriog just outside
Chirk on elevated structures.
The resultant aqueduct of 1800
and railway viaduct of 1848,
built parallel to each other in a
picturesque valley, made an
ideal subject for a saleable print.

[16]
The Moorish Arch
aquatint, hand-coloured
S. G. Hughes after Thomas
Talbot Bury (1811–77)
published by Ackermann & Co,
London, 1832
AE185.809

The architecture chosen to
house the stationary engines
and boilers at Edge Hill on the
Liverpool & Manchester Railway
was described as 'moorish'.
This theatrical style never
became popular again with
railway builders, who preferred
classical Greek, Roman or
Italianate architecture, or
alternatively the fashionable
Gothic Revival.

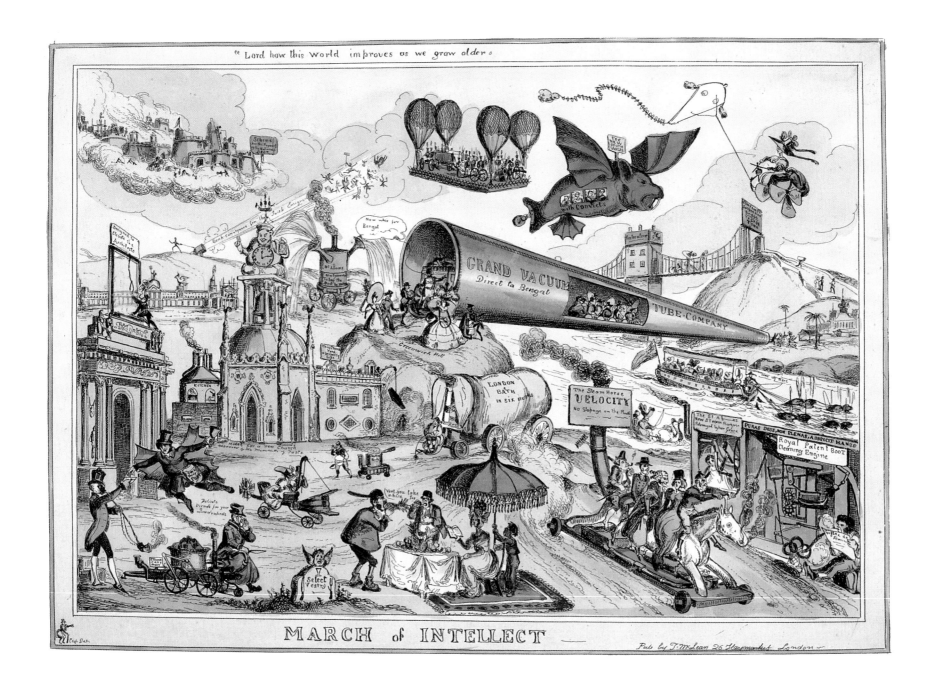

MARCH of INTELLECT

weakness, then it is in relation to the social history of the period. The processes and the products come across as the very obvious achievements of the time; the human condition is more by way of implication. This is not to suggest that Elton made a conscious decision to exclude social history material, but he was certainly more interested in the tangible evidence of industry and transport than its human consequences. Perhaps that was because, as his close friend Sir John Betjeman said of him: 'Arthur mistrusted emotion. I remember him saying of a well-known novelist that she wrote with her stomach and not with her mind.' There is an 1892 edition of Friedrich Engels' *The Condition of the Working Classes in England* (1844), but there are no copies of Factory Acts and very little material on the rise of trade unionism. By comparison there is a good copy of Gustave Doré and Blanchard Jerrold's illustrated book, *London: A Pilgrimage*, published in 1872, which showed the less acceptable side of the urban environment [19]. Elton collected a number of prospectuses extolling the advantages of buying shares in proposed railway projects, but ignored the Board of Trade's official and contemporary reports into railway accidents [20]. On the whole his view of the Industrial Revolution was a positive one, although in his introduction to the Manchester 'Art and the Industrial Revolution' exhibition catalogue of 1968, there is a certain pessimism, perhaps the benefit of a life-time's perspective. But like the engineers, industrialists, scientists and technologists of the 18th and 19th centuries, he was of a generation that still believed in progress. He did not live to experience the uncertainties of the very last years of the 20th century. For the man who had spent his life collecting evidence of the triumph of technology over nature and in the making of films for the Shell oil company, Elton died in the same year as the 'oil crisis' in 1973 — an event which shook the foundations of the industrialised western world. Thirty years later in 2003, having witnessed the death of the British coal industry, the end of large-scale iron and steel production in this country and the privatisation of the railways, it would be fascinating to know what he would think of 'alternative energy' and genetic engineering.

In conclusion, it became very obvious whilst writing this book, that, despite its riches, the Elton Collection remains in a vital way incomplete without its creator. Elton used his collection like an orchestra. Each individual item had its own voice, its own story to tell, but collectively they could be made to play different, coherent pieces of music, with a number of themes and variations. When he revised Klingender's *Art and the Industrial Revolution* in 1968, it was as though he was committing one particular variation, perhaps his magnum opus, to print so that it

[17] opposite
The March of Intellect
etching, hand-coloured
William Heath (Paul Pry)
(1795–1840)
published by Thomas McLean,
London, c1829
AE185.506

[18]
Vanity Set
brass, glass and nautilus shell
mid-19th century
AE185.1834

28

**[20]**
A Collapsed Railway Bridge
pencil and wash drawing, c1850
AE185.61

Although Elton did not collect
official railway accident reports,
he did acquire a few views of early
disasters, this one depicting the
collapse of a bridge.

could be replayed and studied over and over again. But that book was only one performance and it is apparent from the memories of those who knew him that Elton used his collection best in live performances:

'Around him in his Library and Study at Clevedon Court hung a life-time's collection of prints, paintings and drawings of Britain's greatest engineering successes in road, rail and canal. Anyone who had an opportunity of hearing him talk of Brunel or Telford as he pecked at his overflowing shelves, would regard it as a rare privilege and one that would never be forgotten.' (Obituary, *The Antique Collector*, April 1973.)

Ultimately, as with all collectors, many of his careful orchestrations would have been made in private, in his clever mind, without an audience [21]. As documentary film-maker Edgar Anstey said of his colleague:

'Straight from the Highlander in Dean Street this world authority on almost every kind of 19th-century artefact would rush off without warning to lose himself completely in the cataloguing of his unique collection of railway drawings and engravings . . .'

In many ways David de Haan, as the first professional curator of the Elton Collection, continued this performance tradition. His intimate knowledge of the material meant, like Elton, he could extract themes and assemble them for temporary exhibitions, lectures and individual guided tours. Perhaps that is ultimately the best use of the collection, not as a quarry for individual images or texts, but as an experience? Perhaps the collection will always be looking for a new conductor rather than a curator, a worthy successor to the orchestra's founder, Sir Arthur Hallam Rice Elton?

[21]
Railway Accident
pencil drawing
Sir John Tenniel (1820–1914)
AE185.62

Tenniel was a prolific illustrator and did many sketches for the engravers of the magazine Punch to turn into prints. This one shows a skeleton waiting on a collapsing bridge for an approaching train, the finished engraving published in Punch on 1 August 1891. The drawing is said to be the last picture Elton added to his collection.

# 2. Sir Arthur Elton (1906–73)

Sir Arthur Hallam Rice Elton was born on 10 February 1906 in London. His parents were Sir Ambrose Elton (1869–1951), the ninth baronet of Clevedon Court, Somerset, and Dorothy Wynne, whose father, Arthur Robert Wiggin, owned an estate in Ceylon **[22]**.

Clevedon Court had become the family seat in 1709 when Abraham Elton (1654–1727) had purchased the property and adjoining lands. Lying to the east of the town with which it shared its name, the building's origins dated back to the early 14th century. Abraham Elton was a successful merchant in Bristol and in 1705 had established a copper works near Bristol where Abraham Darby I (1667–1717) was a partner before moving to Coalbrookdale in 1708 to make cast-iron pots using a process that was ultimately to revolutionise the British iron industry. Abraham Elton was created a baronet in 1717, serving as MP for Bristol, as did his son and grandson. Down the years, the Eltons gradually withdrew from direct involvement in business, the fifth baronet becoming a curate in West Bromwich whilst the sixth, Sir Charles Abraham Elton (1778–1853), became a classical scholar and poet, his sister marrying the historian Henry Hallam. Sir Arthur Hallam Elton (1818–1883) was a novelist and something of a social reformer, advocating education for all classes. He paid for gas lighting to be installed on the streets of Clevedon and was the first chairman of the Clevedon Pier Company when this new addition to the growing seaside resort was opened in 1869. On his death his nephew, Sir Edmund Harry Elton (1846–1920), became the eighth baronet and it was he who made a name for himself as a Victorian Arts & Crafts potter from 1881 until his death. Completely self-taught, and using a kiln on the estate, Sir Edmund's 'Elton Ware' won medals at international exhibitions in Brussels (1897), Paris (1900) and Milan (1906). His grandson remembered he believed he '. . . was the Chinese answer to William de Morgan'.

Until 1920, when his father inherited Clevedon Court, Arthur Hallam Rice Elton (1906–73) lived with his parents in Bradford-on-Avon **[23]**, served by the Great Western Railway, and in common with many young boys of his generation he became a railway enthusiast. His hobby was

[22]
Bradford on Avon,
Kennet & Avon Canal
oil on board
Sir Ambrose Elton (1869–1951)
AE185.100

Painted by Sir Arthur Elton's
father during World War 1.

**[23]**
The Abbey Cloth Mills,
Bradford-on-Avon
lithograph
James Akerman
AE185.421

The woollen industry in the
West Country never developed
to the same extent as in the
West Riding of Yorkshire, but
it did maintain a hold, and this
mill built in Bradford-on-Avon
in 1875 is an example of one of
the industry's last developments
in this part of Britain.

Abbey Cloth Mills
Bradford-on-Avon
Richard Gane Arch'
6 Mecklenburgh Square W.C.

Sir Arthur Elton (1906–73) – 39

**[38]**
Concurrence
etching
Ernest Bosch (1834-1917)
AE185.432

An evocative scene
somewhere in rural
Germany during
the 1870s.

# 3. The Elton Collection at Ironbridge

After Sir Arthur Elton's death in 1973, the majority of his collection of industrial and transport prints, drawings, books, pamphlets and ephemera, along with a few paintings, were accepted by the Government in lieu of estate duties. An inventory was compiled by his daughter, Julia, and eventually the requisite items were packed in 55 crates and taken to a British Museum store where they remained pending the decision on a new permanent home for the collection. During that time, there were four serious contenders: The Science Museum, London; Bristol City Museum & Art Gallery; the North Western Museum of Science & Technology, Manchester; and The Ironbridge Gorge Museum Trust **[39]**. All these organisations had legitimate reasons for wanting the collection. The proximity of Elton's home at Clevedon Court to Bristol made that city the natural venue if the collection was considered part of the story of a local personality **[40]**. The Science Museum in London was, of course, the national museum for the subject. It already had a large number of librarians who could have looked after the books, but the Pictorial Collection Department, which would have absorbed that material, was very new and not well staffed. The ephemera would have become the responsibility of another department. Manchester, with indisputable Industrial Revolution credentials, had neither storage nor display space, but it did have ambitious expansion plans for its museum service.[2] Ironbridge Gorge Museum Trust was the youngest of all the contenders and although in a similar position to Manchester in not having accommodation immediately available, it had a record of rapid expansion under its charismatic Director, Neil Cossons. Three new museums had opened recently in restored industrial premises, and another — The Museum of Iron in Coalbrookdale — was beginning to take shape. The displays and interpretation methods were progressive and in 1977 the Trust won the Museum of the Year award, followed in 1978 by the accolade of European Museum of the Year. Crucially, as all the Museum sites lay within the boundaries of Telford New Town which was still receiving direct Government funding to complete its expansion plans initiated in 1968, it had active support from Telford

Development Corporation, and was able to call upon this organisation to acquire and restore buildings, underwrite staff posts and provide many other services. The corporation had already assembled a definitive collection of original and secondary source material on the engineer Thomas Telford (1757–1834) **[41]**, a collection housed with the Museum Trust and looked after by a specialist curator. And of all the museums vying for possession, Ironbridge was the only one promising to keep all elements of the collection together, and not to separate the pictorial material from the books and the ephemera.

Uniquely amongst all the contenders, the museums in and around Ironbridge also had another advantage. They were all set within a landscape created by the Industrial Revolution and which had remained little altered since the 18th and early 19th centuries. The landscape of the Ironbridge Gorge and the contents of the Elton

**[39]**
The Iron Bridge
photograph, c1890
AE185.741

One of the first achievements of the new Ironbridge Gorge Museum Trust was raising money in the early 1970s towards the building of a reinforced concrete arch in the river bed beneath the Iron Bridge and other remedial work.

2. These plans did not materialise until the 1980s when the original terminus of the Liverpool & Manchester Railway at Liverpool Road and the adjacent warehouses were converted into an impressive museum complex.

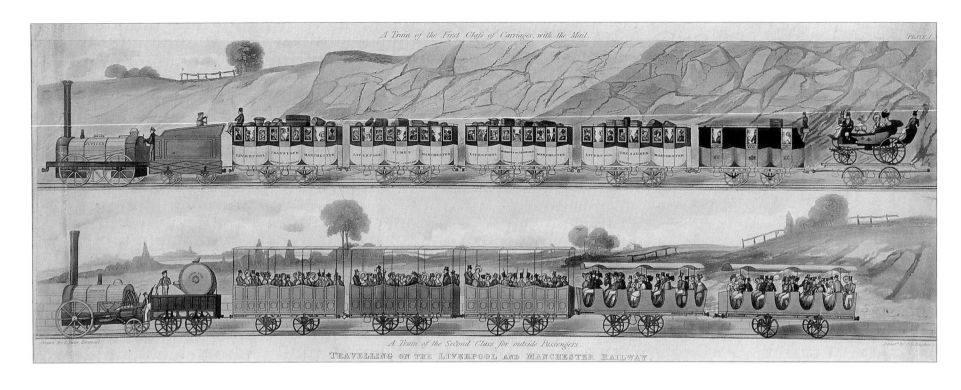

*A Train of the First Class of Carriages, with the Mail.*

PLATE I

LIVERPOOL TRAVELLER MANCHESTER LIVERPOOL TIMES MANCHESTER LIVERPOOL MANCHESTER MANCHESTER LIVERPOOL TREASURER MANCHESTER

*Drawn by T. Shaw, Liverpool.*

*A Train of the Second Class for outside Passengers.*

*Aquat by S.G. Hughes*

TRAVELLING ON THE LIVERPOOL AND MANCHESTER RAILWAY.

**[44]**
Travelling on the Liverpool &
Manchester Railway. A Train of
the First Class of Carriages with
the Mail. A Train of the Second
Class, for Outside Passengers.
aquatint, hand-coloured
published by Ackermann & Co,
London, 1833
AE185.241

One of the original Ackermann
'Long Prints' which reappeared
as chromolithographs over
60 years later in 1894, copies
of the latter also being in the
Elton Collection.

*Drawn by T. Shaw, Liverpool.*

triggered by being taken in his pram to the line where his nurse flirted with a local signalman. The Elton Collection still contains hundreds of postcards of locomotives that he began to collect from an early age [24]. He was also drawn to the still-operational Kennet & Avon Canal [25], and particularly to the gas works. In later life he joked about these three influences on his career — railways, canals and gas works [26].

At Marlborough School he shared his love of the Great Western Railway with John Betjeman (1906-84) at a time when the science and aesthetics of locomotive engineering were in absolute harmony [27]. From Marlborough he went up to Jesus College, Cambridge, studying English and the moral sciences, and it was whilst there that he developed a passion for cinema, becoming film critic for the magazine *Granta*. He was incredibly fortunate that after graduating in 1927 he had the opportunity to combine his interests in both art and technology by moving into the fledgling documentary film industry. His achievements in this field are examined later. At the time he was steadily building up his personal collection of first railway, and then other Industrial Revolution material so that it was inevitable he should become interested in both the academic study and the physical preservation of technology. He became a member of the Newcomen Society in 1935, and after World War 2 chairman of the Centre for the Study of the History of Technology at Bath University. It was under that establishment's aegis that the National Record of Industrial Monuments was set up and based at Bath in 1965.

In 1948 he married Margaret Ann Bjornson (1915–95), daughter of Dr Olafur Bjornson, professor of obstetrics at the University of Manitoba, and the couple had two daughters and a son. In 1951 Elton inherited the family title and estates on the death of his father, and the family moved into Clevedon Court. The decade was spent carefully restoring what he could of the building, until in 1960 it was placed in the care of the National Trust.

In the prime of life, Elton's personality and intellect were as large as his physical appearance. His friend Sir John Betjeman described him as a Viking, whilst another thought of him as 'a finer looking edition of the young Henry VIII'. He dressed casually, which increased his benign giant persona, and the impression left on Keith Vignoles when Elton arrived at the local railway station to visit him during the writing of his book about his great-grandfather, the famous engineer, was of '... a burly bearded figure clutching a bulging carpet bag ...' The incident was so memorable that the author included it in the preface to the finished book [28].

From all accounts, despite his physical stature, Elton was predominantly a gentle and reserved man. According to his friend Stuart Legg, who had worked in the documentary film business with him since 1932, he could also be '... strangely shy with new people, and painfully modest'. He could, however, use his intellectual weight to wound those who opposed him. Another documentary film-making colleague, Edgar Anstey, recalled that occasionally his natural diffidence could give way to pontification: '... Indeed he was sometimes pompous — but a terror to lesser men foolish enough to essay pomposities of their own.' His surviving written works show he was certainly not afraid to express his views, and when reviewing others' books he could be cutting. The final paragraph of his review published in *The Spectator* of O. S. Nock's 1948 book *The Railways of Britain* (Batsford), read:

'Both its charm and its weaknesses come from its shapelessness — charm because Mr Nock introduces, as his feelings incline, all kinds of observations about railways, and bits of gossip about their engineers

[24]
Mumbles Railway
postcard
AE185.1511 (detail)

This postcard from 'Mikey' was sent to 'Piscey' (Elton) at Marlborough School in 1921. As the Oystermouth Railway Co, this line had the distinction of being the first in the country to carry fare-paying passengers in horse-drawn carriages, from 25 March 1807.

[25]
Dundas Aqueduct,
Kennet & Avon Canal
engraving, hand-coloured
J. Shury after William
Williams
published by William
Everitt, Bath
AE185.605

Four miles along the Kennet
& Avon Canal west of
Bradford-on-Avon lies
Dundas Aqueduct,
engineered by John Rennie
(1761–1821), taking the
canal across the River Avon.

[26]  opposite
Bath from Bathampton
watercolour, c1845
Thomas Francis Dicksee
(1819-95)
AE185.9

The Great Western Railway (GWR),
which was one of Elton's passions,
was still in its infancy when this view
of the main line between Bath and
Bathampton was painted. The way
the colour is applied was quite
progressive for its time, anticipating
the work of the French Pointillists
40 years later.

[27]
GWR No 2937 Clevedon Court
photograph

Completed at the Great Western
Railway's Swindon Works in
December 1911, Clevedon Court
was a member of just one class
of various 4-6-0 locomotives
which put the company firmly
in the forefront of locomotive
development until the 1930s.
The engine was withdrawn from
service in June 1953.

[28]
Sir Arthur Elton (1906–73)
photograph, c1970
W. Suschitzky

Elton with his copy of John
Cooke Bourne's History and
Description of the Great Western
Railway, 1846.

and financiers, and pieces of his own professional experience;
weaknesses because the book is anecdotal, and it will be difficult for
the ordinary reader, uninfected by the present-day railway mania
for fact and number gathering, to assess the dynamic part the railway
has played in the history of Great Britain.'

He was equally candid when it came to criticising authors he believed
took too narrow a view of their subject. In his *Sunday Times* review
of L. T. C. Rolt's biography of Isambard Kingdom Brunel published in
1957, he wrote:

'Though Mr Rolt sets out the facts and achievements of Brunel's life
with thoroughness, making illuminating use of materials not hitherto
published, he has to an extent failed to place Brunel in the perspective
of his time, and the book seems a little flat. Whether Brunel knew it or
not, he was a vital part of the social upheavals Mr Rolt says he was too
busy to notice.'

Of his own writings, Stuart Legg recorded emotionally after his death:
'I saw the creative aspects — the sweep of his ideas, his wonderful
individual style of film-making and writing which could crack an egg
with cuts or words with the power of a steam-hammer in reverse.'

The reality was, naturally, somewhat more prosaic. Elton never wrote a book with the same broad scope as his collection or his imagination, nor on the same scale and breadth as his contemporaries who shared his interests. He may have been critical of O. S. Nock, but he never matched his output. Whether that was due to inability, disinclination, a conscious decision not to attempt such a scale of writing, or simply because he did not have the time, we shall never know. His collection and interest in industrial archaeology could, after all, be considered just a hobby. A book that might have come closest to his literary vision, entitled 'The Book of Railways; being a history of the development of the locomotive & its influence on the changing scene', and written jointly with Peter Glemser in the mid-1950s, was still-born.

The 10 books which he did write were a bit like short stories. They were all concise and carefully crafted but never definitive. They were like appetisers, starters prior to a more substantial main course which he never provided. The pair of books produced between the wars certainly whetted the readers' appetite for their subject matter and left them with a desire to find out more. His *Why Aeroplanes Fly*, written jointly with Robert Fairthorne and published by Longmans in 1936, was described in *Today's Cinema* as '... a darned good half-crown's worth', the magazine *Flight* adding: 'The book gives the impression of *1066 and all That*[1] in style, but this is certainly not detrimental to it.' The companion volume, *How Motor Cars Run*, was published in 1939 to accompany a Shell-Mex and BP travelling exhibition.

In the year World War 2 ended he contributed to Collins' 'Britain in Pictures' series with a book entitled *British Railways*. The contents of this slim volume of just 48 pages with eight colour plates and 30 black and white illustrations were bound to be condensed but the balance seemed flawed and the overall result was disappointing. The first 37 pages were devoted to a short history of Britain's railways between the end of the 17th century and 1850. There followed a brief excursion on the Metropolitan Railway, London's first 'underground' railway opened in 1863 **[29]**, and then in just 3,000 words the period of British railway history between 1900 and 1945 was summarily dispatched.

The restrictive format obviously affected the finished product but, by comparison, Elton's best articles benefited from having limited space. 'The Gods Move House', an article written in 1938 for the *London Bulletin*, reads like a narrative poem:

'Formerly romance had flourished among woods and trees. Courtiers and their ladies dressed as shepherds and shepherdesses. In the 19th

[29]
King's Cross Metropolitan Railway Station
chromolithograph, 1864
Kell Brothers
AE185.268

The first section of the Metropolitan Railway between Bishop's Road and Farringdon Street was opened on 10 January 1863. The Great Western Railway ran the service until August that year, and it is two of that company's broad gauge trains that are depicted here.

1. This humorous history of Britain by W. C. Sellar and R. J. Yeatman was first published in 1930 and immediately achieved popular success

Drawing the Retorts at the Great Gas Light Establishment, Brick Lane.

London, Pub.d by Sir Rich.d Phillips & C.o May 1. 1821.

W. Read, Sculp.t

[30]
Drawing the Retorts at the
Great Gas Light Establishment,
Brick Lane
aquatint, hand-coloured, 1821
from One Thousand Experiments
in Chemistry, Colin MacKenzie
published by Sir Richard Phillips
& Co, 1822
AE185.3394

The dramatic moment when
coke was raked out of the ovens
(retorts) at a gas works.

[31] opposite
Primrose Hill Tunnel
watercolour, c1838
John Cooke Bourne (1814–96)
AE185.16

Bourne's work is best known in
monochrome, either sepia wash drawings
used as preliminary sketches for lithographic
prints or the prints themselves. This painting
of Primrose Hill Tunnel just outside Euston
station on the London & Birmingham
Railway, however, shows that Bourne was
also an accomplished watercolourist.

century Romance left Arcady for a railway station. What must have been crude, noisy, dirty machines were idealised. They became filled with nobility and grandeur. They were dainty, commodious and pretty. How glamorous [John Cooke] Bourne makes the entrance to the Box Tunnel. The Flying Carpet became the Flying Drawing Room on wheels.'

Other articles were less self-conscious. At the end of the 1950s he contributed an essay on gas for light and heat for A History of Technology, Volume IV (Oxford University Press) [30] and when his Presidential Address to the Somersetshire Archaeological & Natural History Society was published in the society's proceedings for 1963, 'The Pre-History of Railways', it was a model of academic rigour and presentation. The text was a fascinating piece of research with no less than 52 footnote references showing just what could be achieved by using his collection as source material. Other articles were impressive for other reasons. 'The Piranesi of the Age of Steam', published in Country Life Annual of 1965, for example, was a lean and thoroughly engaging assessment of the work of artist John Cooke Bourne (1814–96). The direct and simple chronicle of this man's output of drawings, paintings and prints immediately ensured the reader's admiration [31]. The facts spoke for themselves.

Elton's greatest literary achievement was his revision of Francis Klingender's ground-breaking 1947 work Art and the Industrial Revolution. The two men were contemporaries, separated in age by only one year and one week, Elton being the older. They remained friends until Klingender's death in 1955. What Elton did for the revised edition, according to his preface, was to trace all Klingender's references back to original sources: '. . . where necessary correcting them and, in many cases, amending, extending or adding to them.' He clarified some of the art historical terminology, amplified large areas of the original text and added many new illustrations from his own collection. He also reinforced the story of the artists, printers and publishers, who had produced the images, elevating John Cooke Bourne, for example, to the same status that Klingender had originally bestowed on Joseph Wright of Derby (1734–97).

To coincide with the publication of the new edition of Art and the Industrial Revolution in 1968, a major exhibition, given the same title as the book, was staged in Manchester City Art Gallery, running from 31 May to 14 July. Three hundred and seventy-three 18th and 19th-century images of industry and transport were drawn from individuals and institutions all over the country but, significantly, 102 of these

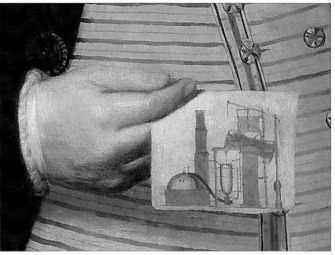

**[32]**
Portrait of a Gentleman Holding
a Drawing of a Steam Engine
oil on canvas, c1780
AE185.169

This painting appeared as No 2
in the Manchester exhibition
catalogue. Unfortunately, the
identity of the sitter is not
known, but he was obviously
very proud of his stationary
engine, to what ever purpose
he had put it to work.

came from Elton's own collection [32]. A 100-page printed catalogue, with 24 black and white illustrations and a six-page introduction by Elton, was issued to accompany the exhibition.

Elton's revision of Klingender's book was much praised. L. T. C. Rolt remarked: '. . . [the original] book would be forgotten today had not Arthur Elton produced a new edition . . . [and] . . . despite its editor's self-effacing modesty, the book is now as much a memorial to Elton as it is to Klingender.' Memorial it may have been, but work of originality it was not. Elton could have chosen to write a companion volume to Klingender's book, but instead he decided to revise it and, consequently, as an operation on someone else's body, it must be judged as such. Whether or not the surgery was successful is open to question. Even if Elton — or anyone else for that matter — had felt certain parts of the original narrative were flawed or, worse still, had become dated, the book was none the less still one person's unique vision. The broad flow of the original was certainly slowed wherever Elton made additions to the text, and in various places the new insertions read like extended footnotes. In architectural terms, an old structure had been given a face-lift and upgraded internal decorations. Perhaps, Elton himself would have made no greater claim for it than that.

Undoubtedly, Elton's true genius was as a film-maker [33]. His first position after graduating in 1927 was with Gainsborough Pictures in London, a company that was barely three years old and the first assistant of which was the young Alfred Hitchcock. Michael Balcon, who had set up the company with Graham Cutts, had a working arrangement with a German film studio, and one of Elton's first assignments was supervising film production in Berlin. After a year he returned to Britain and furthered his knowledge of all aspects of the business until he was made redundant along with other staff in 1930. With that experience behind him, however, he was not out of work for long and in 1931 he was hired along with the young Edgar Anstey by John Grierson, who was then in the process of expanding the film unit of the Empire Marketing Board (EMB). In its short existence, Elton honed his art, directing many of the board's 80 films before it was disbanded and the unit transferred to the General Post Office (GPO) in 1933.

It was during this period that he grew his beard because, to use Anstey's words: '. . . he had obviously decided that as a result of his experiences and meeting Grierson that he was going to become a tough, rough out-of-doors kind of character.'

More importantly, these formative years of his career witnessed the

[33]
Elton Filming in the 1930s

This photograph of Elton on the Great Western Railway is evidence that he learnt his film-making skills from first-hand experiences.

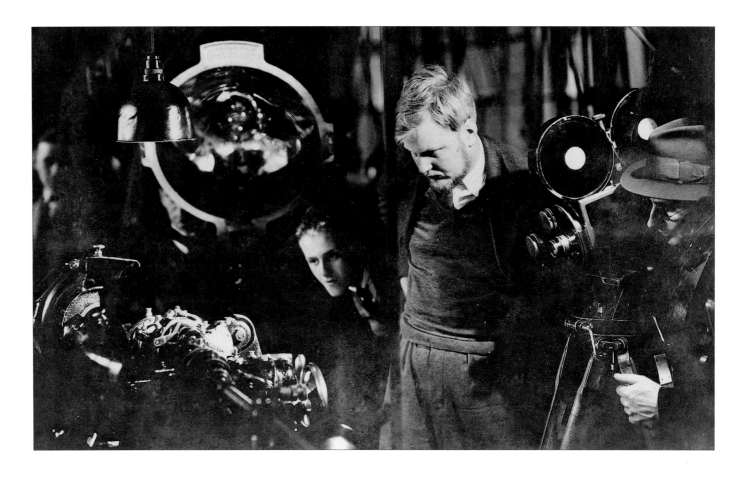

development of his natural ability to collaborate and work successfully with all sorts of people, a talent which John Betjeman drew particular attention to in his obituary. Anstey noted Elton's admiration for craftsmen, especially cameramen.

In 1932 Elton directed two landmark documentary films — *The Voice of the World* about the manufacture of radio-gramophones, and *Aero-Engine* which chronicled the manufacture and testing of aeroplane engines **[34]**. Of the latter Elton later recalled:

'It changed my whole life, in a way, this particular film. I became fascinated with the process and the people. I formed very good relations with the craftsmen themselves, and I never looked back. 'Aero-Engine' gave me a new perspective on films and on what I wanted to do.'

Others were impressed too, and the review in the magazine *Aeroplane* for 1933 concluded:

'After 4,000ft of lovely cinema showing the aero engine being made, the magnificent moment comes: the first flight. For pure visual thrill, and impressionistic beauty, and cinematic value, the sequence of the aeroplane's first flight is unsurpassed.'

The bridge between art and science had been made and, with hindsight, definite parallels can be drawn between John Cooke Bourne's presentation of construction scenes on the London & Birmingham Railway almost exactly one hundred years earlier and the way Elton was crafting his films **[35** and **36]**. Both men recorded their chosen subjects with accuracy as well as a degree of extraction and selective

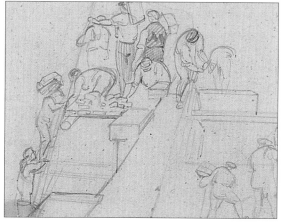

[35 (above) and 36]
Building the London &
Birmingham Railway
pencil and ink drawings, 1836
John Cooke Bourne (1814–96)
AE185.143 and .135 (detail)

focus. Their work was composed but never contrived, photographic but not in an indiscriminate, snap-shot sense of the word. Both men knew how to draw the viewer into a scene, and make the main object of that scene immediately understandable and interesting. And both men made their subject matter heroic [37]. Elton could justifiably be described as a latter-day Bourne with a movie camera.

In 1934 Elton produced and directed *Workers and Jobs*, the first film to include ordinary people talking on camera. Shortly afterwards he left the GPO Film Unit and in 1935 took this development a stage further in the film *Housing Problems* in which the occupants of the Stepney slums spoke for themselves from their own houses directly to the audience. Fifty years after the filming, Anstey recalled: 'It would never have been made if it had not been for Arthur's determination in getting synchronous equipment into these tiny slum houses . . .'

By the time the film was screened in 1936, Elton had set up the Associated Realists Film Producers (ARFP) in London with colleagues from the EMB, and shortly after he was made chief consultant to the Shell Film Unit. This appointment took him away from social realism and refocused his talents on engineering and technology subjects and over the next three years, up to the outbreak of World War 2, he made 16 films for the company. It was these films that really established Elton's reputation in the technical branch of documentary film-making. Basil Wright, another respected practitioner, was moved to write of *Transfer of Power*, made in 1939 as the first of a series on the history of technology, as: 'one of the great historical films in the history of cinema . . . the most wonderful breakthrough in explaining a scientific principle to the world.'

After a brief stoppage at the very beginning of the war, documentary film production at the Shell Film Unit continued. Then in 1940 Jack Beddington from the unit was appointed head of the Films Division of the Ministry of Information and he brought in Elton to become 'Supervisor of Films'. In all, he supervised the production of an astonishing 650 films, some of which had scripts by his old school friend John Betjeman. At the end of 1943, the Scientific Film Association (SFA) was formed with Elton as its first president, and he continued in that capacity until 1946, serving again in the mid-1950s and mid-1960s.

At the end of hostilities, Elton went to Copenhagen for a year as film adviser to the Danish Government, and then in 1947 he was sent to Germany [38] by the Central Office of Information to advise the Central Commission for Germany (British Zone) on documentary film production. As was so often the case, he was not afraid to speak his mind whilst there, and during a broadcast in October that year he set out his simple and direct mission:

'Our job is to see that the films in the new Germany become an independent, healthy and flourishing movement, representative of all that is best in the German people themselves, and not merely an instrument in the hands of those whose principal aim is to get as rich as possible as quickly as possible, and then get out.'

Back in Britain he was made Chairman of the Film Centre in 1948. He also returned to his role as consultant to the Shell Film Unit which, apart from a brief spell between 1957 and 1960 when the company placed him on its payroll as head of the Film & Television Department, he fulfilled until his death. It was during this period that Elton recruited and influenced a new generation of documentary film-makers, many of whom went on to work in television.

Elton was an intellectual film-maker. He was not a mere craftsman. He had a rational explanation for his art, and could place it firmly into an historical framework. During his career he wrote a number of articles and gave talks about documentary films and was particularly keen to have them recognised as historical documents. His lengthy address to the annual conference of the Association of Specialised Libraries & Information Bureaux (ASLIB) at Blackpool in September 1955, entitled 'The Film as Source Material for History', was both a manifesto for the documentary film industry and a heart-felt plea for a more coherent policy for the preservation of its output. The following year he joined the Council of the British Film Archive and one of his last roles was as a member of a working party set up by the Standing Commission to advise on the preservation of technological material. The report was published in 1971, barely two years before his death, containing his contribution on the preservation of photographic, film and sound archives.

Asked to assess Elton's contribution to the British film industry, Stuart Legg remarked:

'In the postwar years — say 1950 to 1965 — Arthur was as important to documentary as Grierson had been previously. And, looking back, I think it is true to say that he brought about a renaissance when it had run out of steam at the end of the war. In effect, he and the oil industry bridged the gap between the era of Grierson and the governments and the rise of BBC/ITV.'

[37]
Kilsby Tunnel
A tinted lithograph from
London & Birmingham Railway
published by Bourne and
Ackerman, 1839
AE185.5677

Sir Arthur Elton (1906–73)  –  45

46

# 3. The Elton Collection at Ironbridge

After Sir Arthur Elton's death in 1973, the majority of his collection of industrial and transport prints, drawings, books, pamphlets and ephemera, along with a few paintings, were accepted by the Government in lieu of estate duties. An inventory was compiled by his daughter, Julia, and eventually the requisite items were packed in 55 crates and taken to a British Museum store where they remained pending the decision on a new permanent home for the collection. During that time, there were four serious contenders: The Science Museum, London; Bristol City Museum & Art Gallery; the North Western Museum of Science & Technology, Manchester; and The Ironbridge Gorge Museum Trust **[39]**. All these organisations had legitimate reasons for wanting the collection. The proximity of Elton's home at Clevedon Court to Bristol made that city the natural venue if the collection was considered part of the story of a local personality **[40]**. The Science Museum in London was, of course, the national museum for the subject. It already had a large number of librarians who could have looked after the books, but the Pictorial Collection Department, which would have absorbed that material, was very new and not well staffed. The ephemera would have become the responsibility of another department. Manchester, with indisputable Industrial Revolution credentials, had neither storage nor display space, but it did have ambitious expansion plans for its museum service.[2] Ironbridge Gorge Museum Trust was the youngest of all the contenders and although in a similar position to Manchester in not having accommodation immediately available, it had a record of rapid expansion under its charismatic Director, Neil Cossons. Three new museums had opened recently in restored industrial premises, and another — The Museum of Iron in Coalbrookdale — was beginning to take shape. The displays and interpretation methods were progressive and in 1977 the Trust won the Museum of the Year award, followed in 1978 by the accolade of European Museum of the Year. Crucially, as all the Museum sites lay within the boundaries of Telford New Town which was still receiving direct Government funding to complete its expansion plans initiated in 1968, it had active support from Telford

Development Corporation, and was able to call upon this organisation to acquire and restore buildings, underwrite staff posts and provide many other services. The corporation had already assembled a definitive collection of original and secondary source material on the engineer Thomas Telford (1757–1834) **[41]**, a collection housed with the Museum Trust and looked after by a specialist curator. And of all the museums vying for possession, Ironbridge was the only one promising to keep all elements of the collection together, and not to separate the pictorial material from the books and the ephemera.

Uniquely amongst all the contenders, the museums in and around Ironbridge also had another advantage. They were all set within a landscape created by the Industrial Revolution and which had remained little altered since the 18th and early 19th centuries. The landscape of the Ironbridge Gorge and the contents of the Elton

2. These plans did not materialise until the 1980s when the original terminus of the Liverpool & Manchester Railway at Liverpool Road and the adjacent warehouses were converted into an impressive museum complex.

[40]
Prior Park, the Seat of
Ralph Allen Esq near Bath
engraving
Anthony Walker (1726–65)
published by John Bowles
& Son, London,
12 December 1752
AE185.792

This is the earliest depiction of a railway in
Britain. The line was promoted by Ralph Allen
(whose large country house is shown in the
background of this print), to connect the stone
quarries at Combe Down to the River Avon at
Bath. Unlike the railways and plateways in the
country's coalfields, it did not develop any
further nor did it spawn any imitators locally,
and remained an isolated initiative.

Collection both illuminated the momentous changes of that period. Stuart Smith, the Museum's Deputy Director & Curator, had already confirmed how inspirational the local landscape had been for artists of the period by compiling the definitive catalogue of images (other than photographs) of Ironbridge and Coalbrookdale.[3] Thanks in no small part to the work of the Museum Trust, the survival of this landscape was eventually recognised by UNESCO in 1986 when the Ironbridge Gorge became the United Kingdom's first industrial World Heritage Site. At its heart, of course, was the Iron Bridge, which ever since erection in 1779 has been the one instantly recognisable monument of its age and symbol of its achievements, a visual testimony to a very British revolution.

In the summer of 1978, Lord Donaldson, then the Labour administration's Minister for the Arts, made the decision to allocate the Elton Collection to Telford Development Corporation on the understanding that professional staff would be appointed, it would be placed in the care of the Ironbridge Gorge Museum Trust and accommodation would be provided immediately.[4] Manchester supporters were very disappointed and Manchester Withington's MP, Mr Silvester, managed to force an adjournment debate in the House of Commons on 18 July 1978. Other critics used the media to express their views. A letter from two gentlemen of the University of Manchester Institute of Science & Technology (UMIST) to *The Guardian* that month declared that:

'. . . Ironbridge is miles from any major population centre. It is a kind of National Park of technology, an industrial Woburn. There is no reason why industrial artefacts and prints should take their place among the lions and lords as part of that British heritage dear to so many car owners . . .'

This was a reference to the safari park established in the grounds of a stately home to encourage more visitors, comparing this development to Ironbridge's open-air museum, which placed buildings in a 42-acre 'park'. Although popular with the general public, Blists Hill Open Air Museum was disliked by many academics.

That Ironbridge did not have the same academic status as Manchester, had been touched on, in a less inflammatory way, by Mr Silvester in his debate. Contrary to popular perception, however, this was not the case. In 1953, Arthur Raistrick PhD, MSc, Extramural Tutor at the universities of Leeds, Durham and Newcastle, had published the first influential study of the Darby family and its association with the Coalbrookdale iron industry. This was a key historical account which

[41]
Thomas Telford (1757–1834)
engraving
W. Raddon (fl 1817–62) after
Samuel Lane (1780–1859)
published 10 January 1831
AE185.584

Telford trained as a mason, gradually using his talents to become one of Britain's greatest civil engineers. In 1787 he was appointed Surveyor of Public Works for the County of Salop, and when his new road between the county town, Shrewsbury, and Holyhead was completed in the 1830s, it was described as: '. . . a model of the most perfect road making that has ever been attempted in any country'.

3. The results of his work were published jointly by Thames & Hudson and the Museum Trust in 1979 under the title *A View from the Iron Bridge*.

4. The Elton Collection was transferred to the Ironbridge Gorge Museum in 1983.

helped to raise the profile of Britain's industrial heritage. Raistrick's enthusiasm also contributed directly to the preservation in 1959 of the remains of the blast furnace where Abraham Darby I's experiments with coke in place of charcoal as a fuel had been successfully carried out in 1709, a crucial breakthrough which enabled the British iron industry to expand enormously from the middle of the 18th century. The blast furnace used by Darby was the first 18th-century industrial monument to be preserved *in situ* and opened to the public alongside a dedicated industrial museum. In 1973 Oxford graduate Barrie Trinder published *The Industrial Revolution in Shropshire*, a meticulously researched history of the many and varied innovations of the Ironbridge Gorge which set the standard for studies on other industrialised regions of the country. As the Museum Trust's Honorary Historian, he followed up the work in 1977 with *The Most Extraordinary District in the World*, a collection of texts by contemporary writers, both from this country and abroad, who, in the 18th and 19th centuries, had recorded their impressions of the industries of the Ironbridge and Coalbrookdale area. What this publication revealed was just how internationally influential the area had been at this crucial period in Britain's history. Dr Trinder became resident lecturer at the new Institute of Industrial Archaeology, established in 1980 as a joint initiative between the Ironbridge Gorge Museum and Birmingham University, the latter awarding postgraduate diplomas and Masters degrees initially in Industrial Archaeology and, later, Heritage Management. In 1983 the institute moved to the Long Warehouse at Coalbrookdale, into the very building restored for the Museum Trust as a permanent home for the Elton Collection.

Other critics of allocating the Elton Collection to Ironbridge focused on the Museum's status as an independent charitable trust which charged admission. In the 1970s the national museums in London, and the great municipal provincial museums, were proud of their socialist tradition of free access. It was an anathema to the directors, custodians and curators of these organisations funded directly by public taxes that a growing number of new independent museums like Ironbridge were financed by gate receipts, donations and grants. Direct comparisons with theatres, opera houses and cinemas (and safari parks) only reinforced the view that these museums were more concerned with entertainment than education, and with audiences rather than visitors. When the Elton Collection was put on display in Ironbridge, admission to the gallery was free.

In the autumn of 1978, three new members of Ironbridge Gorge Museum staff were appointed to look after the Elton Collection and work started immediately on unpacking, cataloguing and photographing the contents. Simultaneously, restoration work was started on the early 19th-century coach house and stables of Rosehill House in Coalbrookdale. By April the Coach House Gallery had been fitted out to display a series of temporary exhibitions drawn from the Elton Collection, and on 21 April 1979 the building was officially opened by Kingman Brewster (1919-88), then American Ambassador to the United Kingdom.

A pattern was established of two themed exhibitions a year using Elton Collection and Museum pictorial material. The themes emphasised the strengths of the Elton Collection, and included in the first few years, 'Early Railways to 1830', 'A Sense of Humour' [42], 'The Marriage of Iron and Glass', 'The Navvies Build' [43], and a display to celebrate the 150th anniversary of the opening of the Liverpool & Manchester Railway (1830–1980) [44].

As well as exhibitions in Coalbrookdale, Elton material was lent to other museums in both this country and abroad. The Museum Trust's extensive collection of Iron Bridge images was augmented with choice pieces of Elton material, brought together with appropriate items borrowed from individuals and public organisations, to form a major exhibition at the Royal Academy, London, in the summer of 1979 to celebration the bicentenary of the erection of the ribs of the Iron Bridge in 1779. Stuart Smith's *A View from the Iron Bridge*, was published to coincide with the exhibition of the same name and became its catalogue.

The new Elton curator, David de Haan, was also keen to use material from the collection in publications. His first project was working on the text and images for Asa Briggs' book *From Iron Bridge to Crystal Palace* (Thames & Hudson) which was also published in 1979 as part of the bicentenary celebrations. David worked with Briggs again to produce *The Power of Steam* (Michael Joseph) in 1982 and other publications followed using Elton material.

In 1983, the Coach House Gallery was closed and from then until the end of the decade, Elton exhibitions were staged in a new gallery in the Long Warehouse, Coalbrookdale. Because of Elton's great love for the Great Western Railway his collection was rich in associated material and, consequently, the Museum Trust was in a unique position in 1985 to play a key role in celebrating that railway company's 150th anniversary [45]. Three years later it was the turn of the London & Birmingham Railway to celebrate 150 years since opening in 1838 and

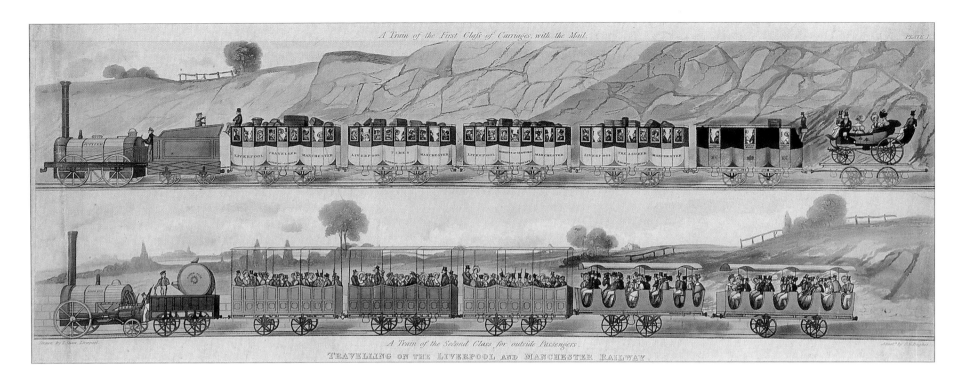

*A Train of the First Class of Carriages, with the Mail.*

PLATE I

*A Train of the Second Class for outside Passengers.*

TRAVELLING ON THE LIVERPOOL AND MANCHESTER RAILWAY.

**[44]**
Travelling on the Liverpool &
Manchester Railway. A Train of
the First Class of Carriages with
the Mail. A Train of the Second
Class, for Outside Passengers.
aquatint, hand-coloured
published by Ackermann & Co,
London, 1833
AE185.241

One of the original Ackermann
'Long Prints' which reappeared
as chromolithographs over
60 years later in 1894, copies
of the latter also being in the
Elton Collection.

52

Elton Collection material, in particular the John Cooke Bourne sketches of construction work, once again allowed the Museum to mount a definitive exhibition.

With hindsight, the allocation of the Elton Collection to the Ironbridge Gorge Museum marked the beginning of a new phase in its development. Until then, as noted above, the Trust was best known for its open-air museum at Blists Hill, where industrial and social history objects were displayed and demonstrated in reconstructed buildings. However, at Coalbrookdale, the Trust pursued a very different educational strategy. The three-storey 1838 Great Warehouse of the former Coalbrookdale Company facing the Old Furnace was turned into the Museum of Iron after a massive restoration project. Opened on 5 July 1979 by HRH The Prince of Wales, it told the story of iron and steel from prehistoric times to the present day, placing the achievements of the local ironmasters — the Darbys, Wilkinsons and Reynolds — into a national framework. A little further north, adjacent to the Coach House Gallery, the two large 18th-century houses built and occupied by the Darbys and other managers of the Coalbrookdale Company Works were restored as Rosehill and Dale House.

During the 1980s, Coalbrookdale developed into a national centre for the study of 18th and 19th-century industry and technology. Following another huge restoration project, the impressive 65m (213ft)-long late-19th-century warehouse adjacent to the Museum of Iron was opened in 1983 to house the Museum's growing research library,[5] archive, all its pictorial collections (including thousands of photographs) and the new Elton Gallery, as well as provide teaching facilities and support accommodation for the recently created Institute of Industrial Archaeology (later renamed the Ironbridge Institute). The Museum's fledgling archaeology unit also made its home in the same building, subsequently producing a series of reports which confirmed the area's national importance historically, whilst at the same time establishing the unit's reputation for the excavation and study of industrial sites in all parts of the country.

Today, the Ironbridge Gorge Museum is a commercially viable business in a crowded heritage market-place. Its 10 sites give visitors, educational groups and researchers the opportunity to explore and better appreciate the industrial legacy of the Industrial Revolution [46], and the Elton Collection remains a key element in that interpretation.

[45]
The Railway Station
pen drawing
William Powell Frith
(1819–1909)
AE185.146

This sketch may have been Frith's original thoughts for the composition of his final, and very famous, painting exhibited in 1862 of the Great Western Railway's London terminus at Paddington. The painting was commissioned by an art dealer and other versions were made as well as large engravings, of which the Elton Collection has a signed example.

5. The museum's existing library collection had become the responsibility of the Elton librarian in 1978

54

# 4. Witness to Change

## The Pictorial Material

At the beginning of the 21st century there can be little doubt that the majority of people make sense of the world predominantly through pictures. There is never a moment when images are not being broadcast around the globe for publication or directly into millions of television sets. Videos and DVDs endlessly replay films and documentaries, sporting events and pornography. There is hardly a human activity that has not been captured on film. All our personal, first-hand experiences, our family memories, our education, are reinforced pictorially. It is far more common now to record our lives by taking photographs and video, than by keeping a written diary. The written word has not been supplanted, but now it is almost always reinforced by illustrations. A tiny proportion of all non-fiction books today contain no illustrations. Perhaps this dependence on pictures can be explained in evolutionary terms if pictorial communication pre-dates writing and, perhaps, even language.

Whatever the prehistory, the fact remains that individuals' understanding of their environment, their interaction with others and their place in society is dominated by the image. In many ways, societies are defined by images. A society can be shaped, given form, or even paraphrased by images **[47]**. The costumes, objects and rituals of pre-industrial

**[46]** opposite
Railway Viaduct
watercolour
William Collingwood Smith
(1815–87)
AE185.32

The London & Greenwich Railway, which opened in December 1836, ran on one continuous 6km (4-mile)-long viaduct of 878 brick arches. It straddled land yet to be developed for housing and industry, as this charming rural scene shows.

**[47]**
Probable Effect of the Projected Railroad to Brighton
lithograph, hand-coloured, c1840
AE185.638

Britain has been a class-conscious society for many years. In the early years of the 19th century the Prince Regent had made Brighton a fashionable retreat for the idle rich, away from the capital and its increasing squalor. This cartoon was a comment for those who were aware how popular travelling along the Liverpool & Manchester Railway had become in 1830, and feared the same might happen if a railway was opened between London and Brighton.

societies were first documented when men like Captain Cook took professional illustrators on expeditions with them. Such pictures influenced our views of other cultures for generations. Once adopted and distributed in popular newspapers and books they created stereotypes which still survive. The early cinema played its part in reinforcing these, 'cowboys and Indians' being just one example.

So invasive and important are images in contemporary life that it is difficult to imagine a time when they were not common currency. In 18th-century Britain, working people would have seen only a glimpse of their country if they had access to the few wood-blocks and engravings that were available. Their everyday lives would still have been dominated by customs moulded by their immediate environment, by beliefs and traditions handed down by word of mouth and by skills learnt on the job. The gentry had the likenesses of their ancestors preserved in oil paint or watercolour, but for the rest of the nation, dead relatives were but a memory. A century later, when railways had

opened up all parts of the country to observation, when periodicals such as The Illustrated London News were widely circulated [48], when people were used to seeing themselves, their relatives and their environment in photographs, and when the moving picture was beginning to record the activity of everyday life, Victorians had a more comprehensive view of their society, even if they deliberately suppressed knowledge of certain aspects of it.

Then as now, however, images have never been purely representational and neither are they completely dispassionate. Any image can be read and interpreted in different ways by different observers. A police photograph of the scene of a road accident aims to be objective; a press photograph of the same scene might be composed so as to shock or evoke an emotion. Many press photographs have achieved the status of art objects and are hung in galleries as such. Today almost any contemporary image (or object) can be considered art if its creator gives it that label. This distinction might seem an unnecessarily

[48]
Arrival of the First Train at Huntly from Aberdeen
wash drawing, 1854
AE185.654 (detail)

This crude drawing, by an anonymous artist, is typical of thousands that were worked up as engravings for publication in The Illustrated London News. The Great North of Scotland Railway between Kittybrewster (Aberdeen) and Huntly opened on 12 September 1854.

abstract diversion in a book such as this, but it is relevant when a visually replete generation like ours has to consider images from a pre-photographic society. The motivation for producing an oil painting in such a society might have been to record a scene as faithfully as possible. The fact that it is physically an oil painting, which today is associated only with art, might make a present-day observer more likely to categorise it as such, when in fact to the society in which it was produced, it was simply a record. The Victorian artist John Cooke Bourne provides an interesting example of this dilemma. To our eyes, there is no doubt that his pencil sketches of navvies at work on the London & Birmingham Railway in the 1830s are works of art which evoke an emotional response [49 and 50]. But did the artist view them as such at the time, or if he had had a camera, would he have simply photographed the scene? The artist produced the sketches both as a response to the exciting activity of the moment and as a record of manual labour, as references that might be useful in later works. Bourne never elevated his sketches to the status of art by working them up as paintings or lithographs in their own right. A generation later, S. W. A. Newton used his camera to record the extension of the Manchester, Sheffield & Lincolnshire Railway between Nottinghamshire and London, Marylebone. Like Bourne he was excited by the events unfolding around him and interested in the work of the navvies, but he never considered himself an artist. Yet there is no doubt his images have subsequently been given the status of those of J. C. Bourne. But are they art?

There is no definite answer to this question, and throughout the Elton Collection there are tens of drawings, paintings and prints, which straddle this soft-focus line between record and art. Sir Arthur himself said: 'To some extent I share the view that the artist ought to take his place in life as a craftsman. We're all so sick of artists who think that they're so important.' This remark was made at a time when abstract and non-representational art had become the orthodoxy, when theory was held in higher regard than practical technique. But Elton's comment might equally have applied to the great Victorian artists who, although always representational and believing the techniques they used were as important as the subject matter, had in the social climate of their own times become establishment figures, and had elevated themselves above the status of mere craftsmen.

There are no great works of art in the Elton Collection. It is arguably stronger for it. The images are more honest and closer to their subject matter and, therefore, less pretentious. Only a handful of paintings

[49 and 50]
Building the London &
Birmingham Railway
pencil and ink drawings, c1836
John Cooke Bourne (1814–96)
AE185.128 and .133 (detail)

transcend their subject matter so that the finished work is a purely visual experience. The best example of this is William Collingwood Smith's (1815–87) watercolour which uses a coalmine on the Northumberland coast as an excuse for an exercise in atmospheric painting [51]. This work is a truly picturesque English watercolour, firmly in that tradition, and comparable with similar late work by J. M. W. Turner, for example. Although it is not an abstract picture nor impressionistic in the way this term was applied to the work of the late 19th-century French school of art, it is certainly not representational, nor truly topographical. It is, however, unusual in the collection.

Finally, it must not be forgotten that almost all the pictures in the Elton Collection were originally produced for financial gain, either to commission or for the commercial market. They were not produced for the sake of art [52]. They were images crafted for sale, and, consequently, most tend to show their subject matter in a favourable light. It is true many are important social documents, but they can never be taken as completely objective records. They were not photographic representations of their subjects. They were intended either for display or as conversation pieces in the collections of connoisseurs and because of this they conformed to the artistic conventions of their day, often deliberately incorporating certain conventional elements into the scenes to make them acceptable to their clients. There is George Robertson's 1788 painting of 'The Inside of a Smelting House at Broseley', for example, produced as a commercial print by the engraver Wilson Lowry [53]. Painted during the Romantic phase of British art, what was in fact an up-to-date blast furnace is made to look old and dilapidated, the light generated by man's toil as the molten metal flows into the pig-bed contrasted with the light of the moon, a symbol of the powers of nature. In 'A View of the Tanfield Arch', I. C. Stadler's coloured aquatint of 1804 after Joseph Atkinson's watercolour [54], the influence is the romantic, idealised, classical landscapes of the painter Claude Lorraine (1600–82), well-known to the British art market through reproduction prints. The arch takes the place of some ancient and heroic ruin from a lost civilisation which it would have been if painted by the Frenchman. The fact the arch was not depicted when it was built in 1726, but over 70 years later when it was falling into disuse, is an indication of what the artist knew was acceptable as the subject matter for such a large print at the time. The product of a later generation, W. Humber's 1850 watercolour of Welwyn viaduct, appears to have no such pretensions in its straightforward depiction of its subject. But looking at the other

[51] opposite
A View of Tynemouth
watercolour
William Collingwood Smith
(1815–87)
AE185.73

An atmospheric shore scene with a coalmine in the middle distance and, just visible in the background, Tynemouth Castle. The artist was part of a very strong British watercolour tradition which was associated with the likes of J. M. W. Turner (1775–1851), Thomas Girtin (1775–1802), David Cox (1783–1859) and Peter De Wint (1784–1849), to name but a few.

[52]
Building Work at Kensington, London
etching, c1890
Joseph Pennell (1860–1926)
AE185.416

One of the few items in the Elton Collection which was produced as a conscious 'work of art'; in other words, the artist was more interested in the compositional opportunities presented by the cranes rather than by the cranes themselves or what they were doing.

elements of the painting, the sheaves of corn and, in the foreground more prominent than the train crossing the railway structure, a faithful dog guarding the farm workers' vittles [55], is not the work in fact an idealised pastoral idyll which happens to have a viaduct in the background? Edward Duncan's large watercolour of the Eastern Counties Railway at Ely certainly makes the observer question the role of the railway in that scene [56]. So prominent is the Romanesque cathedral and so insignificant the railway, perhaps the latter is fulfilling the role of the dog in Humber's work.

All these points need to be considered when looking at the pictorial material in the Elton Collection. The images are far from being the innocent observations of artists and engravers. They are not objective photographic records, but products of their times and all the more interesting for that fact. We, too, need to be aware that our perceptions are also coloured by the standards of our own age and our interpretations of the scenes will be different from those of their original creators.

[55]
Welwyn Viaduct
watercolour,
September 1850
W. Humber
AE185.164

This viaduct was one of the most impressive structures on the Great Northern Railway's main line between London and Doncaster. The section between the capital and Peterborough was officially opened on 8 August 1850, but three days before that the directors were treated to a journey across the viaduct in a train hauled by two locomotives, just visible in this painting.

**[56]**
Ely Cathedral from
the Railway
watercolour, c1850
(attrib) Edward
Duncan (1804–82)
AE185.141

The 11th and 12th-century cathedral, with
its 14th-century octagonal lantern and
choir, dominates this view, its fabric at the
time of the painting in the throes of
restoration by the most notable Victorian
architect in this field, George Gilbert Scott
(1810–78). Dwarfed by this example of
earlier engineering is an Eastern Counties
train approaching from the east.

# Books and Pamphlets

Elton started collecting books from an early age and there are numerous volumes in the collection which bear witness to his boyhood interest in railways [57]. By his own admission, it was collecting Great Western Railway engine numbers and particularly learning their names which encouraged him to read for himself. When he was 14 he attended a jumble sale at Marlborough Town Hall and bought a copy of W. M. Acworth's *The Railways of England* for just 2d. In the years that followed he quickly added other classic Victorian and Edwardian editions to his growing collection. Then in 1930 he purchased Dendy Marshall's new book *The Centenary History of the Liverpool & Manchester Railway*, published by the Locomotive Publishing Company to celebrate the 100th anniversary of the opening of that influential railway. Marshall's scholarly approach to this work greatly impressed Elton, but so too did the fact that the author was an avid collector of all sorts of early railway ephemera. Elton followed suit and began to build his own collection.

The legacy of that collecting in relation to books and pamphlets falls into two main categories: primary and secondary material. A large part of the book collection is made up of the latter, books written by authors who, although they may have used primary sources, were certainly not present during the events they chronicle. These were the sort of works Elton started to collect as a boy, and continued to add to his collection up to his death. Some of these books will remain useful and others will be of interest only to students of Elton's life and times because they reflect the views of his generation. No interpretation of historical events can be completely objective. All authors are children of their own time, influenced by its events and values and their own experiences. Klingender was a self-confessed Marxist and when he compiled his *Art and the Industrial Revolution* after World War 2 the world was only just emerging from the devastating consequences of Fascist dictatorships. Consequently, and inevitably, Klingender made sense of the British Industrial Revolution from a political perspective, as well as from that of an outsider, someone who would probably have felt he had more in common with the Quaker Darby's in Coalbrookdale than with Winston Churchill, a product of the British establishment. Klingender's view of the past has itself become history. Theories about the causes and particularly the consequences of industrialisation have changed, just as have all other aspects of history. The past is now filtered through the

intellects of new post-industrial historians who have access to new material which alters perceptions and leads to new interpretations.

The strength of Elton's library rests, therefore, with those texts written by commentators with first-hand experience of their subject matter. These books and pamphlets will retain their significance and, perhaps, increase in importance. As just one example, there is a wealth of contemporary texts on the various plans for a tunnel under the English Channel, the earliest being a French document of 1869 — '*Project de construction d'un tunnel sous-marine pour establissement d'un chemin de fer devant relier La France à L'Angleterre*' — supported by English publications of the 1880s and, later, between 1907 and 1918. There are many other topics with similar quality material but as it would be impractical to provide a comprehensive list here, the table on Page 68 lists a few of the more significant titles.

Many of these publications, as well as being contemporary written accounts, were also well illustrated. Elton was especially fortunate in the quality of illustrated books he acquired, in particular those volumes which, although bound as books, were principally collections of prints. The most famous examples in the collection are the two volumes of lithographs by John Cooke Bourne of the London & Birmingham Railway (Bourne & Ackermann, 1839) [58 and 59] and the Great Western Railway (David Bogue, 1846). Equally important, though more mannered than Bourne's realistic views, are Thomas Talbot Bury's beautifully executed hand-coloured aquatints of scenes on the London & Birmingham Railway published by Ackermann of London in 1837 [60] as a companion edition to his earlier views of the Liverpool & Manchester Railway. The latter, issued initially as a collection of seven hand-coloured aquatints, appeared in February 1831. The edition was completed in July that year with the addition of a further six plates, and then published as a whole in 1832. By then the plate of Wapping Tunnel, at the Liverpool end of the line, had been reworked so as to change the original steam locomotive with train into a cable-hauled train of wagons. Elton acquired all three variations of this print, showing the transformation [61, 62 and 63]. Of other railways, the collection has a good edition of A. F. Tait's *Views of the Manchester & Leeds Railway*, made up of 19 lithographs published in 1845. There is also a copy of David Octavius Hill's *Views of the Opening of the Glasgow & Garnkirk*

**[58 and 59]**
[58] Building the Stationary
Engine House, Camden Town
and [59] Bridge Near Euston
Station, from London &
Birmingham Railway
lithograph, tinted
John Cooke Bourne (1814–96)
published by Bourne &
Ackermann, 1839
AE185.5677

# The Elton Library: Significant Titles

*History of the Cotton Manufacture*, Edward Baines Jr, c1841 (AE185.2980)

*Comparative advantages of the atmospheric railway system*, Peter Barlow, 1845 (AE185.3982)

*Specification of John Birkinshaw's patent for improvement in the construction of malleable iron rails to be used in railroads*, John Birkinshaw, 1822 (AE185.3904)

*The History and Antiquities of the Town and County of Newcastle-upon-Tyne, including an account of the coal trade*, John Brand, 1789 (AE185.4910 and .4911)

*Railway Practice; a collection of working plans and practical details of construction in the public works of the most celebrated engineers*, S. C. Brees, 1837 and 1840 (AE185.2686 and .2687)

*The History of Inland Navigations*, James Brindley, 1766 (AE185.2307 and .2308)

*A Brief Account of Some Travels in Hungaria, Serbia, Bulgaria; with observations on the gold, silver, mineral waters, etc, in those parts*, Edward Browne, 1673 (AE185.4949)

*The Britannia & Conway Tubular Bridges, with general inquiries on beams & properties of materials used on construction*, Edwin Clarke, 1850 (AE185.2236 and .2237)

*Architecture of Machinery: an essay on propriety of form and proportion, with a view to assist and improve design*, Samuel Clegg Jr, 1842 (AE185.2405)

*Observations on a Tour through almost the whole of England* (two volumes), C. Dibdin, 1801 (AE185.5166)

*On the Use of Hot Air in the Iron Works of England & Scotland*, N. Dufrenoy, 1836 (AE185.5238)

*The Principles of Mechanics*, W. Emerson, 1758 (AE185.3613)

*Encyclopaedia Britannica*, Vol I (reprint of 1786), Vol II and III, 1786, (AE185.3072–.3074) and six volumes of the fourth, fifth and sixth editions, 1824, (AE185.3075–.3080)

*L'automobile*, Henri Farman, Paris, c1902 (AE185.3720)

*Voyage en Angleterre en Ecosse et aux Iles Hebrides; avant pour object les sciences, l'histoire naturelle et les Moeurs*, B. Faujas-Saint-Fond, Paris, 1797 (AE185.5159 and .5160)

*Lectures on select subjects in mechanics, pneumatics, hydrostatics and optics with the use of globes*, James Ferguson, 1773 (AE185.3410)

*Great Exhibition: Royal Commission for the exhibition of the works of industry of all nations*, four volumes bound in full morocco, 1852 (AE185.3148–.3151)

*Recollections of the Great Exhibition of 1851*, 25 chromolithographs with hand colouring published by Day & Sons (AE185.5286)

*Observations on steam carriages on turnpike roads; returns of daily practical results of working; etc*, Goldsworthy Gurney, 1832 (AE185.2748)

*Remarks on the proposed railway between Birmingham and London, proving by facts and arguments that work would cost 7.5 million; that it would be a burden on the trade of the country, and would never pay*, Investigator, 1830 (AE185.4855)

*Voyages métallurgiques*, Gabriel Jars, three volumes 1774–81 (AE185.5262–.5264)

*Lectures on the steam engine*, Dionyseus Lardner, four volumes, 1832 (AE185.2736–.2739)

*Interborough rapid transit; the New York subway, its construction and equipment*, 1904 (AE185.4435)

*Journal of 2$^1/_2$ years residence in Great Britain*, Jehangeer Nowrojee and H. Merwanjee, naval architects, 1841 (AE185.4877)

*General view of the agriculture of Shropshire*, Joseph Plymley, 1813 (AE185.5647)

*Railway Chronicle*, 1845 (2 volumes), 1846, 1848 and 1849 (AE185.4130–4134)

*The Cyclopaedia*, Abraham Rees, 39 volumes of text and six volumes of plates, 1819 (AE185.3100–.3144)

*Reports made in the course of his employment as a civil engineer*, John Smeaton, four volumes, 1812 and 1814 (AE185.2939–.2942)

*Reports on canals, railways & roads*, William Strickland, Philadelphia, 1826 (AE185.3154)

*The Channel Tunnel; military aspects of the question*, Lord Sydenham of Combe (House of Commons), 1914 (AE185.2559)

*The Steam Engine*, Thomas Tredgold, 1827 (AE185.5273)

*Plans of several lines of railway in Ireland, laid out under direction of the Commissioners*, Charles Vignoles & John MacNeill, 1837 (AE185.2251)

*System of familiar philosophy in twelve lectures*, A. Walker, two volumes, 1802 (AE185.3396 and .3397)

[60]
Bridge over the canal near
Kings Langley
From Six Coloured Views on the
London & Birmingham Railway
aquatint, hand-coloured
J. Harris (d 1834) after Thomas
Talbot Bury (1811–77)
published by Ackermann & Co,
18 September 1837
AE185.4158

[61, 62 and 63]
The Tunnel
aquatints, hand-coloured
H. Pyall (fl 1820–40) after
Thomas Talbot Bury
(1811–77)
published by Ackermann,
1831
AE185.237–.239

Trains were hauled through Wapping
Tunnel, Liverpool, by stationary steam
engines positioned at Edge Hill
(Moorish Arch) which was something
the artist did not at first appreciate.
It took two alterations to his original
plate to completely eradicate the
locomotive. The figures in the tunnel
were correct as hundreds of visitors
were admitted before the line opened.

*Railway*, 1832 and Andrew Nichol's *Five Views of the Dublin & Kingstown Railway*, issued in 1834. Of the non-railway material, one of the most interesting, though less well known, is R. Rawlinson's *Designs for Factory Furnace and Other Tall Chimney Shafts*, published in 1858 **[64]**.

All the books and pamphlets, in all the categories mentioned above, like the individual images in the Elton Collection, provide their own perspective on the Industrial Revolution. As with the images, there is an obvious bias towards the technology rather than the social history of the period, but that is not just because Elton was selective. It indicates how technology truly did take precedence over people in this revolutionary period. The quantity and the specialist content of this material also reflects how increasingly complex working life became from the 1750s onwards. Master and worker no longer worked with a few simple tools which could be easily described in a few words and with simple diagrams. During the late 18th century and throughout the 19th century machinery became increasingly complex. It was no longer the product of simple trades such as joinery, iron-casting and blacksmithing. The new machines were the products of specialist designers who demanded specific tolerances in the material used and who indicated these requirements on complex plans and elevations drawn by teams of specialist draughtsmen. Once assembled, the machines demanded specialist attention from a new breed of worker, each with his or her own specific task which often demanded a degree of training, sometimes with the aid of specialist books. The same was true in civil engineering. In the 18th century building the Bridgewater Canal was a leap of faith by its poorly educated but intuitive engineer, James Brindley **[65]**. By the end of the Victorian era his successors were well-educated professionals who understood the science of their work and expressed themselves in mathematical equations and in technical drawings, entrusting the execution of their ideas to specialist contractors with teams of skilled workmen. This fundamental change is clearly discernible in the books and pamphlets of the Elton Collection.

In conclusion, although these books and pamphlets are a serious resource for students of the Industrial Revolution, it is also good to be able to record that a great deal of pleasure, and insight, can be had not just by consulting the rare and important volumes in the collection but by searching out the odd and slightly eccentric material. There is, for example, what was purported to be one Rochdale man's account, written entirely phonetically for the full effect, of his visit to the Great Exhibition of 1851, entitled: 'Oful, tru, un pertikler okeawnt of bworth aw seed un wat aw yeard'. The working class was a constant source of

**[64]**
Designs for Factory
Furnace and Other Tall
Chimney Shafts
lithograph, tinted
R. Rawlinson
(1810-98)
published by Kell
Brothers, London,
1858
AE185.5300

A number of chimneys disguised
as fine Italian campaniles or
other Gothic towers were erected
in various parts of Britain, but the
majority of 18th and 19th-
century factory and mill
chimneys were uncompromising
shafts of engineering brick or
stone.

[65]
James Brindley (1716–72)
mezzotint, 1833
Henry Cook after Francis
Parsons FSA
AE185.749

Born in Derbyshire, Brindley
became a millwright and
erected Newcomen steam
engines before agreeing to
engineer the Bridgewater Canal
for Francis Egerton (later the
third Duke of Bridgewater).
He followed this achievement
with the Trent & Mersey Canal,
also known as the Grand
Trunk Canal.

interest for Victorian society and it is not surprising, therefore, that Albert H. Bencke could write a 16-page article in the 1884 *Belfast Newsletter* entitled 'Bridging the Irish Channel, considered with reference to the third class passengers'. Other writers drew attention to the dangers of those who attempted to rise above their station in life. For instance, Alfred Crowquill published a pictorial 'skit' on George Hudson (the 'Railway King') in 1849, after the great man's creative accountancy skills had led to his public disgrace, called: 'How he reigned and how he mizzled; a railway raillery' [66]. Travel obviously fascinated authors and gave rise to some interesting texts. One that sounded almost philosophical appeared in 1753, written by R. Griffiths and published under the title, 'A profound meditation upon Turnpikes'. A hundred years later, a piece entitled 'A trip through the Caledonian Canal and tour in the Highlands', appears to be a straightforword text until the reader discovers it was privately published in 1861 by someone using the pseudonym 'Bumps'. Perhaps this writer's Scottish journey had been uncomfortable but it was obviously not as dangerous as that which inspired another mid-19th-century author to write a little eight-page document called, 'The importance of a constant preparation for death, illustrated by the narrative of an accident on a railway'. Both these travel books make Elton's copy of the Eastern Counties Railway timetable for Colchester for 1845 seem surprisingly reassuring [67].

[66]
George Hudson (1800–71)
lithograph, tinted, 1845
(attrib) Richard Doyle
(1824-83)
AE185.568

# Eastern Counties Railway

## TIME TABLE.

☞ **Passengers are recommended to be at the Stations five minutes earlier than the time specified in the Table, which is the approximate time only.**

*September 1st, 1845.*

### COLCHESTER LINE.

**DOWN TRAINS.—(Sundays excepted.)** / **SUNDAY TRAINS.** / **FARES.**

| Distances from London | LONDON to COLCHESTER | 3rd Cls. A.M. | A.M. | A.M. | 3rd Cls. & Goods P.M. | P.M. | P.M. | P.M. | P.M. | P.M. | Mail. P.M. | Sun A.M. | Sun A.M. | Sun P.M. | Sun P.M. | Sun P.M. | Quick 1st | Quick 2nd | Ord 1st s. d. | Ord 2nd s. d. | Ord 3rd s. d. |
|---|---|---|---|---|---|---|---|---|---|---|---|---|---|---|---|---|---|---|---|---|---|
| | London | 7 30 | 8 30 | *11 0 | 12 30 | 1 30 | 3 0 | 4 15 | 5 30 | 6 30 | 8 30 | 8 30 | 9 45 | 2 0 | 4 0 | 8 30 | | | — | — | — |
| 1 | Mile End | 7 35 | 8 34 | — | — | 1 34 | — | — | — | — | — | 8 33 | 9 48 | 2 3 | 4 3 | — | | | — | — | — |
| 4 | Stratford | 7 48 | 8 41 | 11 11 | 12 46 | 1 43 | — | 4 26 | 5 41 | 6 41 | 8 40 | 8 43 | 9 58 | 2 13 | 4 13 | 8 40 | | | 0 9 | 0 6 | 0 4 |
| 7 | Ilford | 8 0 | 8 49 | 11 18 | 1 0 | 1 50 | 3 16 | 4 33 | 5 48 | 6 48 | 8 46 | 8 51 | 10 6 | 2 21 | 4 21 | 8 46 | | | 1 4 | 1 0 | 0 7 |
| 12 | Romford | 8 20 | 9 1 | 11 30 | 1 22 | 2 2 | 3 28 | 4 45 | 6 0 | 7 0 | 8 56 | 9 4 | 10 19 | 2 34 | 4 34 | 8 56 | | | 2 6 | 1 9 | 1 0 |
| 18 | Brentwood | 8 42 | 9 15 | 11 45 | 1 46 | 2 17 | 3 43 | 5 0 | 6 15 | 7 15 | 9 11 | 9 20 | 10 35 | 2 50 | 4 50 | 9 11 | | | 3 6 | 2 6 | 1 6 |
| 23½ | Ingatestone | 9 2 | 9 31 | — | — | — | — | 5 16 | — | — | 9 35 | 9 37 | | | 5 7 | 9 35 | | | 5 0 | 3 6 | 2 0 |
| 30 | Chelmsford | 9 45 | 9 44 | 12 12 | 2 34 | — | 4 12 | 5 29 | 6 42 | — | 9 49 | 9 52 | | | 5 22 | 9 49 | | | 6 6 | 4 6 | 2 6 |
| 35 | Hatfield | 10 3 | 9 57 | — | — | — | — | — | 6 55 | — | — | 10 6 | | | 5 36 | — | | | 7 6 | 5 3 | 2 11 |
| 38½ | Witham | 10 25 | 10 7 | 12 34 | 3 10 | — | 4 33 | — | 7 4 | — | 10 13 | 10 16 | | | 5 46 | 10 13 | | | 8 6 | 6 0 | 3 3 |
| 42 | Kelvedon | 10 43 | 10 17 | 12 44 | 3 26 | — | 4 43 | — | 7 14 | — | 10 23 | 10 27 | | | 5 57 | 10 23 | | | 9 0 | 6 6 | 3 6 |
| 47 | Marks Tey | 11 10 | — | 12 54 | — | — | — | — | 7 24 | — | — | 10 38 | | | 6 8 | — | | | 10 0 | 7 0 | 3 11 |
| 51 | Colchester | 11 25 | 10 45 | 1 13 | 4 5 | — | 5 11 | — | 7 45 | — | 10 49 | 11 0 | | | 6 30 | 10 49 | | | 11 0 | 7 6 | 4 3 |

* This Train calls at Ingatestone on Fridays.

**UP TRAINS.—(Sundays excepted.)** / **SUNDAY TRAINS.** / **FARES.**

| Distances from Colchester | COLCHESTER to LONDON | Mail. A.M. | A.M. | A.M. | A.M. | A.M. | P.M. | P.M. | 3rd Cls. P.M. | P.M. | 3rd Cls. & Goods P.M. | Sun A.M. | Sun A.M. | Sun P.M. | Sun P.M. | Sun P.M. | Quick 1st | Quick 2nd | Ord 1st s. d. | Ord 2nd s. d. | Ord 3rd s. d. |
|---|---|---|---|---|---|---|---|---|---|---|---|---|---|---|---|---|---|---|---|---|---|
| | Colchester | 2 45 | N.B. | | 9 0 | 11 0 | 3 0 | | 5 0 | 6 0 | 7 0 | 2 45 | 8 30 | | 4 0 | | | | | | |
| 4 | Marks Tey | — | | | 9 10 | — | 3 10 | | 5 12 | — | — | — | 8 52 | | 4 22 | | | | 1 0 | 0 7 | 0 4 |
| 9 | Kelvedon | 3 10 | | | 9 22 | 11 22 | 3 22 | | 5 34 | 6 22 | 7 36 | 3 10 | 9 3 | | 4 33 | | | | 2 0 | 1 3 | 0 9 |
| 12½ | Witham | 3 20 | | | 9 32 | 11 32 | 3 32 | | 5 49 | 6 32 | 7 52 | 3 20 | 9 14 | | 4 44 | | | | 2 6 | 1 9 | 1 1 |
| 16 | Hatfield | — | | | 9 45 | — | — | | 5 58 | 6 45 | — | — | 9 24 | | 4 54 | | | | 3 6 | 2 4 | 1 4 |
| 21 | Chelmsford | 3 45 | | 8 45 | 9 59 | 11 54 | 3 54 | | 6 24 | 6 54 | 8 28 | 3 45 | 9 38 | | 5 8 | | | | 4 6 | 3 2 | 1 9 |
| 27½ | Ingatestone | 4 3 | | 8 54 | — | 12 8 | ‡ | | 6 50 | 7 8 | — | 4 3 | 9 53 | | 5 23 | | | | 6 2 | 4 0 | 2 4 |
| 33 | Brentwood | 4 23 | 8 40 | 9 10 | 10 25 | 12 23 | 4 22 | 5 30 | 7 26 | 7 23 | 9 14 | 4 23 | 10 10 | 1 0 | 5 40 | 8 0 | | | 7 6 | 5 0 | 2 9 |
| 39 | Romford | 4 38 | 8 56 | 9 26 | 10 41 | 12 39 | 4 37 | 5 45 | 7 53 | 7 39 | 9 33 | 4 38 | 10 26 | 1 15 | 5 56 | 8 16 | | | 8 6 | 5 9 | 3 3 |
| 44 | Ilford | 4 48 | 9 6 | 9 38 | — | 12 49 | 4 47 | 5 55 | 8 13 | 7 50 | 9 58 | 4 48 | 10 39 | 1 26 | 6 9 | 8 29 | | | 9 8 | 6 6 | 3 8 |
| 47 | Stratford | 4 54 | 9 14 | 9 46 | * | 12 58 | 4 55 | 6 3 | 8 25 | 7 58 | 10 14 | 4 54 | 10 47 | 1 33 | 6 17 | 8 37 | | | 10 3 | 7 0 | 3 11 |
| 50 | Mile End | — | — | 9 52 | † | — | — | | 8 38 | 8 4 | — | — | 10 58 | 1 40 | 6 26 | 8 46 | | | 11 0 | 7 6 | 4 2 |
| 51 | London | 5 4 | 9 27 | 10 3 | 11 11 | 1 12 | 5 11 | 6 19 | 8 45 | 8 15 | 10 35 | 5 4 | 11 0 | 1 45 | 6 30 | 8 50 | | | 11 0 | 7 6 | 4 3 |

On Wednesdays the Train marked thus * stops at Stratford, and the Train marked thus † at Mile End, to take up and set down Passengers.

‡ This Train calls at Ingatestone on Fridays.

N.B.—This Train starts from Colchester on Monday Mornings at 5 minutes past 7, calling at all the intermediate Stations, except Ingatestone and Mile End.

J. T. Norris, Printer, 138, Aldersgate Street.

**[68]**
Jigsaw puzzle, London
& Birmingham, and
Liverpool & Manchester
Railways
c1840
AE185.1877

Charming though this jigsaw
puzzle appears to us today, it
must be remembered that at
the time it was issued railways
were the most modern form of
transport available.

# Ephemera

The variety of material Elton collected in this category gives us yet another fascinating insight into contemporaries' views of their society [68]. As with the pictorial material mentioned above, almost all the items were made for financial gain so there must have been a market for their subject matter. The majority were only part of a larger output of their particular manufacturer and obviously Elton was selective and collected only those pieces with industrial and transport themes. But even with these provisos, their survival does indicate what interested people at the time.

Some of the choicest items are pieces of pottery. They range from high-quality hand-painted bone china to mass-produced creamware decorated with single-colour transfer prints. The latter are some of the earliest examples of the cheap and popular 'souvenir' or commemorative items, a category of decorative pieces of which the most famous became the ubiquitous 20th-century coronation mug. The fact that so many of these pieces were decorated with railway images shows not only how popular the new transport was but also how such subject matter had become acceptable for display in the home. These items could be afforded by many working-class families, and they represent some of the first non-functional items that ordinary people felt justified spending their hard-earned money on purely for decorative purposes.

Of the higher quality items, the Elton Collection contains two particularly attractive pieces with hand-painted decoration: a small, single-handle, bone china mug with a view of the Iron Bridge [69] dating from the 1820s or 1830s, and a bone china fruit bowl or cake stand of about the same date with a central image of Thomas Telford's Menai Suspension Bridge [70]. Not of the same artistic merit but a rarer item is the earthenware jug decorated with a blue and white transfer print of the Brandling Junction Colliery Railway [71] and of equal importance are the mug and bowl with transfer prints proclaiming 'Success to the Paris Mine Co' [72] (see p135).

Finally, there are the mass-produced ceramics. Railway subjects on these pieces date back to the first years of the 1830s, following the unprecedented success of the Liverpool & Manchester Railway which opened on 15 September 1830. The demand for trips on the new line was obviously matched by the demand for souvenirs. Many of these were either glazed creamware jugs or mugs, by then standard products

[71]
Creamware jug decorated with
transfer print of the Brandling
Junction Colliery Railway
AE185.1785

of many factories in the Potteries area. The first pieces were, on the whole, larger than those which followed, with good-quality transfer prints, which implies that they were aimed at a more discerning 'collectors' market than the later pieces. Subjects ranged from depictions of the locomotives involved in the Rainhill Trials of 1829 to views on the line, one of the most popular being of the Moorish Arch at Liverpool. Although the engine *Novelty* entered at the trials by Braithwaite and Ericsson failed to win the competition, it became a favourite with the spectators, and this is reflected in the fact that the Elton Collection contains five pieces with transfer prints of this locomotive compared with only one of *Rocket*, the superior and triumphant machine **[73]**. The most popular railway image produced after 1830 was of a 2-2-2 steam locomotive, often named 'Express' **[74]**. This engine was usually shown pulling a few carriages through a rural landscape and, on pottery (mugs, jugs and cups), was very often stretched or compressed to fit around the shape of the host item. There is little doubt that the items with this image represented the cheap souvenir end of the market. The same image was also used on two-dimensional printed material, for example, as a heading for railway advertisements in the popular press, and long after the actual locomotive type had become old-fashioned, it continued to be the image of choice if the subject of railways had to be illustrated.

As well as pottery, the Elton Collection also contains a few choice examples of 19th-century glassware. The best of these are pieces of Sunderland glass and the finest is a large bell-shaped goblet or rummer on a stem containing a silver coin, the main body engraved with an image of the Sunderland Bridge of 1796 on one side and Stephenson's Newcastle High Level Bridge of 1850 on the other **[75]**.

More numerous, but like the glass in the collection, far from a definitive selection, are the trade tokens and medallions. Of the 76 items, the most important are those commemorating Marc Isambard Brunel (1769–1849) and the Thames Tunnel and the Great Exhibition. Of the rest, there are a few interesting medals from a number of countries including Argentina, Austria, Belgium, France and Holland; most celebrate the opening of some of these countries' first railways.

The remainder of the ephemera collection is a fascinating mixture of objects. The most exotic is a porcelain coffee percolator mounted on a brass, four-wheeled chassis, the whole piece made to resemble an early locomotive **[76]**. Another item which was produced as a response to the popularity of the Liverpool & Manchester Railway is a papier

**[72]**
Creamware bowl and mug
decorated with transfer print
'Success to the Paris Mine Co'
1790s
AE185.1815, and .1816

**[73]**
Bone china cup decorated with
transfer print of steam
locomotives Rocket and Novelty
1830s
AE185.1778

**[74]**
Earthenware mug decorated
with transfer print of 2-2-2
steam locomotive Express
1860s
AE185.1787

**[75]**
Large glass rummer engraved
with views of the High Level
Bridge, Newcastle upon Tyne
and the Sunderland Bridge
1850s
AE185.1772

[76]
Porcelain coffee percolator in
the shape of an early steam
locomotive
J. B. Toselli & Cie, Paris
1850s
AE185.1833

mâché tray painted with a view of the Moorish Arch at Liverpool [77]. There are a number of Stevengraphs — machine-made embroidered pictures — with railway subjects [78] as well as half a dozen snuff boxes decorated with the outlines of early locomotives.

No part of the ephemera section of the Elton Collection forms a definite collection in its own right, and for this reason a specialist collector would probably dismiss Elton's three-dimensional items as lacking coherence. But Elton did not try to assemble the best collection of trade tokens, nor did he go out of his way to collect Sunderland glass rummers, or railway buttons of every class of employee working for every pre-1923 railway company in Britain (and there are modern collectors who aspire to achieve the latter). Assessing what items he did collect by these criteria is not relevant. Elton did not collect objects for what they were as objects. He saw them very much as an integral part of the whole collection, and this can be illustrated very clearly with the following example. In its planning and during its construction in the 1820s and 1830s, the Thames Tunnel became a topic of some fascination to both engineers and the general public alike. The endeavour was probably not as difficult as the excavation 50 years earlier of the 1½-mile-long Harecastle Tunnel (see p111) on the Trent & Mersey Canal by Brindley's navvies between 1766 and 1777, nor did it claim as many lives (26 men) as did the building of the 3-mile long Woodhead Tunnel for the Sheffield, Ashton-under-Lyne & Manchester Railway (between 1839 and 1845), started before the Thames Tunnel was completed. But the London enterprise obviously captured people's imagination because a variety of material was produced at the time which was not the case for the Harecastle and Woodhead tunnels. There were prints of the actual tunnel with both English and German texts, contemporary descriptions of the work in English, Danish and Norwegian, a number of commemorative medallions [79] and a stoneware spirit flask moulded with a representation of the stairs leading to the tunnel. All these items Elton brought together in his collection, and added to them a portrait of the Thames Tunnel's engineer, Marc Brunel [80], and various reports of the directors (1828 and 1839), so that collectively, the survival of all these objects provided a unique perspective on the whole undertaking. This is just one example of what Elton achieved in his collection and, therefore, despite its size and variety, the pottery, glass, trade tokens, medallions and other ephemera are not just crucial to the collection but crucial to an understanding of it and, in many ways, to an understanding of the man who assembled it.

[77]
Papier mâché tray, with hand-painted view of the Moorish Arch, Liverpool & Manchester Railway
c1831
AE185.1850

The image on this tray was copied from an engraving by Isaac Shaw showing the celebrations in Edge Hill cutting on the opening day of the Liverpool & Manchester Railway on 15 September 1830.

[78]
George Stephenson:
Pioneer of Railways
Stevengraph
c1887
AE185.96

**[79]**
Medallion commemorating the opening of the Thames Tunnel, 1843.
AE185.1932

**[80]**
Marc Isambard Brunel
(1769–1849)
mezzotint
James Carter after Samuel Drummond (1765–1844)
published by F. Gwynne, London, 7 October 1846
AE185.559

As well as his work on the Thames Tunnel shown in the background of this print, Brunel also invented machines for mass-producing army boots and ship's rigging blocks, small but significant contributions to Britain's military supremacy in the 19th century.

[81]
North Midland Railway
Bridge Under the Cromford
Canal at Bull Bridge
lithograph
S. Russell
published by Day & Haghe,
c1850
AE185.270

This was the sort of scene where the SHIC
system proved its worth. The print contains
a number of elements which different
researchers might want to find in a
catalogue: aqueducts; the Cromford Canal;
the North Midland Railway line between
Derby and Normanton; early steam
locomotives; working horses; turnpike
roads; men working; rivers; etc.

# 5. Record of a Revolution

With the appointment of a professional librarian to catalogue the Elton books in 1978, the decision was made to use the specialist UDC system which was more appropriate to their subject matter than the more widely used Dewey Decimal arrangement. When this author became responsible for cataloguing the remainder of the collection in the same year, he and the curator felt a similar specialist system should be adopted for the pictorial material. At the time, university research projects at Cambridge and Manchester were demonstrating that computer cataloguing with the capabilities of powerful individual word searches was close to becoming a reality, but in the short term Ironbridge would have to implement a manual system. As with a library system, what was needed was a classification that would give the staff the ability to group items not just by artist, medium or date but also by the subject matter [81]. An assessment of existing classifications was made but this revealed that all had been devised for specific collections and many museum systems lacked intellectual rigour. Coincidentally in the same year as the Elton Collection was allocated to Ironbridge, Peter Brears, then curator of the York Castle Museum, had called a meeting to discuss the creation of a subject classification for museums, in which objects would be grouped primarily according to their use and not by their maker, material or medium. The result was the formation of a working party of like-minded people of which the Curator and Documentation Assistant of the Elton Collection became key members. Over the next four years the group worked together to create the Social History & Industrial Classification (SHIC) which was eventually published by the Centre for English Cultural Tradition & Language, University of Sheffield, in 1983. SHIC quickly established itself in the museum profession and the pictorial element of the Elton Collection was the first to be catalogued using the new system.

Since then, of course, computers have developed very rapidly, negating the need for sophisticated classification systems. All details of the Elton Collection are now held on computer in the Ironbridge Gorge Museum's Library & Archive, and can be subjected to complex searches. SHIC is now an interesting historical document in its own right, reflecting the views of a group of young curators in the early 1980s coming to terms with how best to preserve and make intellectual sense of a society once dependent on heavy industry.

Despite the appropriateness of SHIC and the endless possible listings available from clever computer software, because the theme of this book is the Elton Collection and it is as much a reflection of the man who put the material together as the subject matter of that material itself, the following images are presented under the headings used in the 'packing catalogue'[6] which accompanied the collection when it first came to Ironbridge. Unlike SHIC, in which every category was carefully and logically subdivided as the result of hours of intellectual debate, the packing catalogue was far less complex. It was, as its name implies, simply a list of brief descriptions of those items placed in storage awaiting final allocation to the chosen repository. The subtleties of interpretation that Elton would have been able to extract from every item in his collection are certainly not reflected in the headings used in the packing catalogue. But, nevertheless, it remains a genuine link with the collector himself, and has validity for that reason alone.

6. The 'packing catalogue' was compiled by Sir Arthur's daughter, Julia Elton, and it was presented to the museum in two, seven-volume, editions. The first was bound with board covers and interleaved with a number of professional black and white and colour photographs of selected items. The second was the equivalent of a paperback edition and became the everyday working tool for the new Elton staff at Ironbridge.

[82]
Penrhyn Slate Quarries
lithograph, hand-coloured
J. Newman (1786-1859)
AE185.757

An illustration of the effects
of large-scale quarrying in
North Wales.

[83]  opposite
Carding, Drawing and
Roving: Mule Spinning
engraving from Baines's
History of the Cotton
Manufacture, 1835
J. Tingle after T. Allom
(1804–72)
AE185.2980

Of six, seven and eight-year-
olds, Robert Owen wrote in
1831: '. . . it was absolutely
necessary that the children
should be employed within
the mills from six o'clock
in the morning till seven in
the evening, summer and
winter . . .'. In 1833
Parliament prevented
children under the age of
nine working in factories.

# Topography

The economic fuse that had been ignited in the first half of the 18th century in disparate parts of Great Britain set off an explosion of industrial development in the following century. From the 1750s onwards the rural and urban landscape that had been changing gradually for centuries underwent accelerated transformation. Up and down the country, in villages, towns and cities, there had always been workshops of all kinds with craftsmen and women working in a variety of materials to satisfy local markets. What the entrepreneurs of the Industrial Revolution did was to transform these crafts into manufacturing industries by encouraging specialisation, concentration, and, most importantly, by expanding their scale. The new goal was the creation of a surplus, an output which could satisfy not just a local demand but also a national and, ultimately, an international one. To achieve this increased output it was essential to have more efficient production methods, better sources of power, a controllable workforce and access to transport for the raw materials coming in and the finished products going out. Where once industrial activity had sat comfortably in the landscape as an integral part of it, by the end of the 18th century it was increasingly altering that landscape for its own ends [82]. In agriculture the steady improvements in farming methods, enclosure of land, the rotation of crops, careful breeding of livestock, etc throughout that century and into the next, changed the countryside just as fundamentally as manufacturing districts were being transformed. The visual impact of these changes was to be seen all over the country.

What soon became the most recognisable evidence of industrialisation was the multi-storey factory. By the end of the 19th century it had become the ubiquitous building in which any product could be mass-produced, and there was hardly a town in Britain that did not have a factory of some sort. But the design had its origins in the textile industry and, for the first 100 years after its appearance at the beginning of the 18th century, the factory was invariably associated with water-powered mills. Arguably the first such building was erected at Derby in 1702, a three-storey structure where silk-spinning machinery was driven by a waterwheel. A larger building, five storeys high to accommodate machines tended by 300 workers, was erected alongside a few years later, and this was truly the precedent for all subsequent mills.

Developments first in cotton and worsted spinning in the 18th century and then in weaving in the 19th century were the impetus for large-scale mill building. Richard Arkwright's (1732–92) water-powered cotton spinning mills in Cromford, Derbyshire, became places of pilgrimage for writers and artists.[7] Travellers wanted to see the huge waterwheels that drove the clever machinery that had been invented to replace manual labour. They wanted to see the self-contained community of workers assembled like a foreign tribe to service that machinery [83], all their needs, including housing, provided by the management. And most importantly they travelled to see how the multi-storey mills looked in the landscape, what effect they had on the scenery. As these buildings multiplied and as more was understood about the living and working conditions in and around these factories the awe changed to disgust. In the following century, when the steam engine liberated factories

7. The mills on the River Derwent became a World Heritage Site in 2001.

from their dependence on water and they began to dominate many urban landscapes, mills lost their appeal and became symbols of all that was bad about industrialisation.

Textile mills and multi-storey factories created completely new working environments for thousands of people during the Industrial Revolution and the same was true for the most important extractive industry of the period — coalmining. Coal was the primary source of energy in the Industrial Revolution and in the coalfields of the Midlands, the North East **[84]**, South Wales **[85]** and Scotland, the small coal pits and adits worked by a few men reliant on candles and a horse gin for winding the coal to the surface were replaced by larger collieries which exploited ever deeper seams as the 18th and 19th centuries progressed **[86]**. These collieries needed steam engines to pump water from the workings and bring the coal out, screens for grading the coal and wagons running on iron rails to move it to the rivers, canals and the sea for export **[87]**. The whole environment around the pit-heads changed completely as huge quantities of spoil were piled into man-made mountains and rows of houses were built not just for the miners but for all the other associated tradesmen necessary to keep these coal-winning machines working around the clock.

The coalfields also acted like magnets, pulling in other industrial activities. Once coal was found suitable when coked as a fuel for blast furnaces, ironworks multiplied, encouraging the development of new processes which needed a new skilled workforce to carry them out. By the end of the 18th century the commons around the South Staffordshire and North Worcestershire mines **[88]**, for example, were populated by numerous metalworkers. In the triangle of land between Wolverhampton, Stourbridge and Birmingham, the scattered settlements grew into untidy towns, each with their own specialities: locks in Willenhall, chains in Cradley Heath and lorinery in Walsall. Long before Queen Victoria passed through the area with the blinds of her carriage window drawn down, the Black Country had made its mark on the landscape.

The same was true of the ironworks in Coalbrookdale. There the foundries were set in a deep natural wooded valley which was the ideal place for the 18th-century traveller to experience nature (art) and industry together and exercise the fashionable philosophies of the Romantic and the Sublime **[89]**. Many saw the beauties of the natural environment despoiled by the works of man. Others believed they were witnessing the taming of nature for the good of mankind. But no matter

[84] opposite
A Northumberland Colliery
wash drawing, 1840
James Wilson Carmichael
(1800–68)
AE185.108

An atmospheric view of an almost entirely man-made industrial landscape.

[85]
Coalworks
watercolour, signed and dated 1791
John Hassell (1767–1825)
AE185.173 (detail)

Coalmining in South Wales had, by the end of the 19th century, completely transformed many valleys. Before that happened, Hassell was able to record the landscape at the end of the 18th century. Prominent is the horse gin for winding men and materials to and from the underground workings.

[86]
Coalworks. A View near
Neath in Glamorganshire
aquatint, hand-coloured
John Hassell (1767–1825)
published by F. Dulas,
London, 28 February 1788
AE185.412

Another picturesque view by Hassell
of a Welsh coalmine. Next to the
horse gin, the smoking chimney
indicates a Newcomen steam engine
was probably being used to pump
water out of the mine.

**[87]**
The East Prospect
of Whitehaven
engraving, hand-coloured, 1738
Richard Parr after Mathias Read
AE185.399 (detail)

The port of Whitehaven was a
planned development of the
1670s and 1680s, a product
of the 'commercial revolution'
that witnessed Britain's
establishment as a world trading
power by the start of the 18th
century. When first established,
coal was one of the port's
principal exports.

**[88]**
A Staffordshire Colliery
wood engraving
W. H. Prior
AE185.448

A typical 'Black Country'
mine in the early 19th
century.

what their views, it was the visual spectacle they came to experience. The drama of the activity, the relentless blasts of the bellows, the slapping of the waterwheels, the alternative charging and then tapping of the open-topped furnaces and the piles of coking coal lighting up the night sky were all fuel for their imaginations.

If the ironworking districts were red with flaming furnaces and black with smoke, so too were the regions making pottery. The proliferation of coal-fired bottle kilns in these areas ensured that. In North Staffordshire so dominant did this particular industry become in the 19th century that the area became known simply as 'The Potteries'. This was due in

no small part to the energies of Josiah Wedgwood (1730–95) who introduced division of labour production methods to the pottery industry in 1769 when he opened his Etruria factory. As with Abraham Darby's ironworks in Coalbrookdale or Arkwright's mills in Cromford, Etruria soon attracted tourists.

The factory was located on the new Trent & Mersey Canal, of which Wedgwood was one of the leading promoters. Like so many other entrepreneurs, he realised that improvements in transport were essential if industry was not to suffocate. First canals and turnpike roads then railways [90], particularly from the 1840s onwards, all left

**[90]**
Port Madoc from the
Embankment
lithograph, hand-coloured,
1849
AE185.200

In 1807 William Madocks (1773–1828)
began to build a mile-long embankment
across the mouth of Traeth Maw so that
slate from the Ffestiniog quarries could
be brought down to a new port being
developed at Port Madoc. In 1814 a
tramway was built across what was
termed 'The Cob', as shown in this print.

**[91]**
South East View of the Cast-iron
Bridge over the River Wear
engraving, c1796
A. Hunter after R. Johnson
AE185.403

The foundation stone of this
bridge was laid in September
1793 and the completed
structure was opened on
9 August 1796.

**[92]**
East View of the Cast-iron
Bridge over the River Wear,
at Sunderland, Previous to the
Centre Being Taken Down
aquatint, c1795
J. Raffield (fl 1795–1825)
after Robert Clarke
AE185.411 (detail)

This print was dedicated to
Rowland Burdon, MP for
Sunderland, patentee of the
construction method used for
making this bridge and director
of the firm in Rotherham,
Walkers, which cast the
individual boxes making up
the arch.

[93]
Pontcysyllte Aqueduct
aquatint
J. Bluck after J. Baker
AE185.400

indelible marks on the landscape, both directly and indirectly. The erection of the Iron Bridge in 1779 over the River Severn near Coalbrookdale was promoted as a way to improve links between the industries either side of the river. A wooden bridge could have achieved the same objective, but what the bridge proved was the suitability and durability of iron as a structural material, and its fame was as much for this, and its aesthetics, as its function. The success of the material persuaded others to build iron bridges. In 1796 the River Wear was crossed at Sunderland by a bridge assembled from iron wedge-shaped boxes [91 and 92]. Images of the resultant impressive structure appeared as prints, transfers on pottery and as engravings on local glassware. Barely 10 years later, one of the greatest feats of the

engineers Thomas Telford and William Jessop (1744–1814) was to take a ¾-mile section of the Ellesmere Canal 38.8m (127ft) high over the Dee Valley in North Wales in a cast-iron trough [93]. The Pontcysyllte Aqueduct which opened in 1805 altered the landscape there in the most dramatic way possible, and, like the Iron Bridge and the Sunderland Bridge, it became a subject for both writers and artists.

After engineering the Caledonian Canal in Scotland, opened between 1818 and 1822, Telford was given the task of surveying the road between London and Holyhead, the Government's vital communications artery with Ireland. The improvements through Wales left a legacy of well-designed bridges in both iron and masonry. But the most graceful

[94]
The Wonders of the Menai
lithograph, hand-coloured,
1850
J. Fagan after S. Hughes
AE185.183

A view showing both Thomas
Telford's road suspension
bridge of 1826, and Robert
Stephenson's later tubular
railway bridge of 1850.

structure which immediately attracted the attention of artists because
of its beauty was Telford's suspension bridge across the Menai Strait
**[94]**. Opened on 30 January 1826, it had a clear span of 176.5m (579ft)
between the two piers. This figure is significant because only three
years later, Telford, then 72 years old, rejected 23-year-old Isambard
Kingdom Brunel's (1806-59) plans for a suspension bridge with
almost twice that span across the Avon Gorge outside Bristol **[95]**.
So concerned was the older man, that he submitted his own design,
with two massive Gothic towers rising from the floor of the gorge **[96]**.
Brunel modified his plans as a result of Telford's concerns to win the
design competition but never lived to see his Clifton Suspension Bridge
finished. When it was finally completed and opened in December 1864,

it truly became a monument to this great man, his fellow professionals
having salvaged the chains from his Hungerford Bridge over the Thames
**[97]** when that structure was demolished in 1862, and paid for the
remaining work needed at Clifton.

Brunel's greatest civil engineering achievements, however, were for
railway companies. There was his daring brick arch of Maidenhead
Bridge which took the twin tracks of his 7ft gauge Great Western
Railway across the River Thames in 1839 **[98]**. The terminus of that
railway when it reached Bristol was a monument to his talents as an
architect **[99]**. His innovative bridge across the River Wye at Chepstow
opened in 1852 **[100]** was followed by the more impressive structure

[96]
Mr T. Telford's Design for the
Suspension Bridge across the
River Avon from St Vincent's
Rocks to Leigh Down
lithograph
published by Wright & Bagnall,
Bristol
AE185.379

[95]
Gateway of Clifton
Suspension Bridge
lithograph
W. Gauci
published by O. C. Lane, c1830
AE185.383

A realisation of the Egyptian
architectural style Brunel
planned for the brick and
stonework of his suspension
bridge.

over the River Tamar at Saltash for the Cornwall Railway, completed in 1859 and christened the Royal Albert Bridge **[101]**. Elsewhere on the South Devon and Cornwall railways, with limited finances, he resorted to timber for the numerous viaducts required, demonstrating he could work just as well in that material **[102]**.

Brunel's contemporary and friend, Robert Stephenson (1803–59) **[103]**, though less flamboyant, rivalled Brunel for innovation in bridge building design. In 1850 he completed two extraordinary bridges of very different types. To cross the Tyne in Newcastle he engineered a novel bridge for both rail (opened August 1849) and road (opened February 1850) traffic made up of six cast-iron bow string girders **[104]**, and then for his Britannia Bridge across the Menai Strait for the Chester & Holyhead

Railway he decided upon wrought-iron tubes. The tracks passed through these tubes, the design of which had been subjected to both exhaustive theoretical and practical tests by William Fairburn (1789–1874) and Professor Eaton Hodgkinson (1789–1861) **[105]**. The three main towers had actually been built with bearings for suspension chains if it was felt that they were needed. In the event they were not.

Whilst Stephenson and Brunel stood at the pinnacle of their profession, there were many other Victorian engineers creating equally impressive railway structures all over Britain, each one altering the landscape. Sir William Cubitt (1785–1861) and his son Joseph (1811–72) used traditional masonry construction for the 476m (1,563ft)-long Digswell or Welwyn Viaduct across the Mimram Valley built for the Great

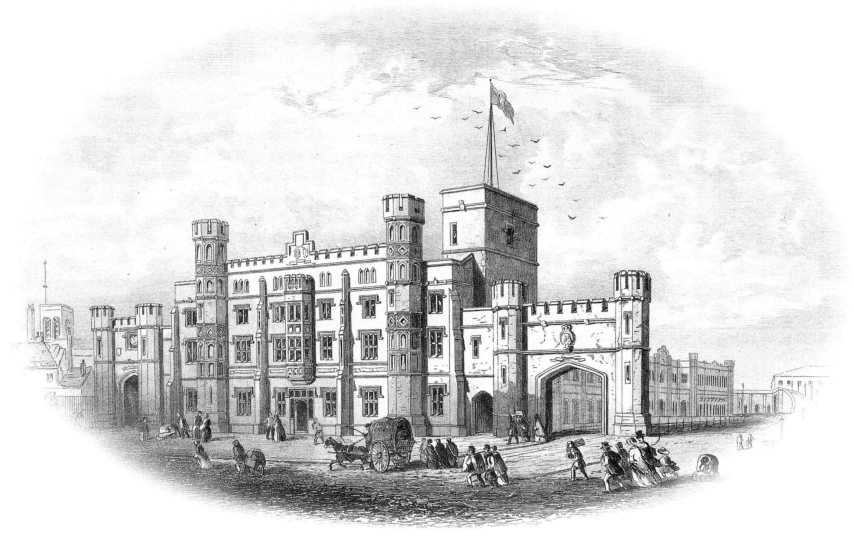

[99]
Bristol Railway Station
engraving, c1850
A. Ashley after J. F. Burrell
AE185.703

Brunel chose the Tudor Gothic
style for the Great Western
Railway's terminus at Bristol.

100

[100]
Chepstow Bridge
lithograph, tinted and hand-coloured
W. Richardson (fl 1842-77)
published by Robert Taylor,
Chepstow, August 1851
AE185.318

In many ways this bridge over the River Wye was a prototype of the larger bridge at Saltash, opened at the end of the decade. In both structures, the railway was suspended from the wrought-iron tubes, all the metalwork being prefabricated on the shore and then floated into position. The bridge at Chepstow lasted almost exactly 110 years until it was replaced in 1962.

[101]
The Opening of the Royal
Albert Bridge, Saltash
oil on canvas, 1859
Thomas Valentine Robins
AE185.131

This was I. K. Brunel's last work,
and on the opening day, 2 May 1859,
because he was so ill, he was drawn
slowly across the bridge on a
specially prepared platform truck.
Steaming 30.5m (100ft) beneath
was the Royal Yacht, Britannia,
shown in this painting with
HRH Prince Albert on board.

[102]
Gover Viaduct
watercolour
H. Geach
AE185.1

This timber viaduct was
one mile west of St Austell
on the Cornwall Railway,
engineered by I. K. Brunel.
The structure was replaced
with a masonry one in
1898.

[103]
Robert Stephenson
engraving
D. J. Pound after a photograph
by J. E. Mayall
AE185.581

Northern Railway and opened in 1850 (see p62). At the end of that decade, Thomas Kennard (1825-93) chose a metal lattice structure for his Crumlin Viaduct which strode 61m (200ft) high and 550m (1,800ft) in length above Ebbw Vale. It opened in 1857 [**106**]. Progress and success seemed assured when Thomas Bouch's (1822–80) 2-mile-long Tay Bridge opened in June 1878, the Queen conferring a knighthood on the engineer for this achievement [**107**]. But a year and a half later it collapsed, taking belief in ever greater feats of railway building with it. It was not until the opening of the huge cantilevered bridge designed by (Sir) Benjamin Baker (1840–1907) and (Sir) John Fowler (1817–98) to cross the Forth Estuary over 10 years later in 1890 that confidence was restored. The first bridge to be built entirely of steel, it immediately became one of the wonders of the world and the railway age has no better monument than the Forth Railway Bridge [**108**].

Almost all these examples of railway engineering were constructed away from centres of population and, indeed, at the beginning of Queen Victoria's reign, the railways often stayed a discreet distance from the ancient centres of towns and cities they were meant to serve. However, by the middle of the century their cuttings and embankments were beginning to form the boundaries for new and endless rows of working-class terraced housing and middle-class villas and by the dawn of the new century railways had thrust their way unabashed into all parts of the urban environment. In 1838–9 the Midland Counties Railway had built its Nottingham station in open fields, half a mile to the south of the town perched on a sandstone outcrop above the flood plain of the River Trent [**109**]. Sixty years later the Manchester, Sheffield & Lincolnshire Railway cut directly through the very heart of that settlement, removing thousands of tons of rock and erecting substantial brick and steel viaducts to the north and south, connected by tunnels to an extensive new sunken central station.

By 1900 when that central station, Nottingham Victoria, opened, all British towns, ports and cities had been transformed, not just by railways but by the construction of new factories, warehouses, churches, chapels, schools, town halls, libraries, shops and houses. During the 19th century new districts had emerged that had not existed before, suburban growth following the railways out of town. Not all settlements had been affected in equal measure. Some towns had continued to prosper quietly as market centres, whilst others had stagnated, unable to compete with rivals with the advantage of a new railway connection, or access to better raw materials or with a speciality manufacturing capacity. But all had been affected to a greater or lesser

**[104]**
High Level Bridge,
Newcastle upon Tyne
lithograph, hand-coloured
George Hawkins
(1810–52) after James
Wilson Carmichael
(1800–68)
published by E. & J. Bruce,
Newcastle, 1849
AE185.790

Plans for a 'high-level' bridge across the
Tyne dated back to 1839 when a
laminated timber road bridge had been
proposed. Within a few years, George
Stephenson and George Hudson became
involved, and the design was modified so
that it could be used as both a road and
railway bridge. The final structure was
designed by Stephenson's son, Robert,
aided by Thomas Harrison (1808–88),
work starting in October 1846.

[105]
Britannia Tubular Bridge over
the Menai Strait, Showing the
Floating of the Second Tube,
3 December 1849
lithograph, tinted
George Hawkins (1810–52)
published by Day & Son, London,
July 1850
AE185.819

Eight wrought-iron timber-lined tubes, the
longest being 143m (470ft), were needed
to complete the railway link between the
mainland and the island of Anglesey.
Riveted together on the shore, each tube
was floated out to the base of the towers
and then hydraulic presses were used to
gradually raise them to their final position,
masonry being inserted beneath as they
ascended.

[106]
Crumlin Viaduct
lithograph, tinted and hand-
coloured
Maclure, Macdonald &
Macgregor after H. J. Cooke
AE185.332

Sketched by H.J Cooke

CRUMLIN VIADUCT,
ON THE TAFF VALE EXTENSION OF THE WEST MIDLAND RAILWAY,
CONSTRUCTED EXCLUSIVELY OF IRON. LENGTH 1658 FEET. HEIGHT 200 FEET
Designed and Erected by T. W. Kennard Esq C E.

extent. A number of towns in the industrial heartland of the country had expanded to the size of cities, and some were eventually granted city status. Birmingham, for example, which was made a city in 1889, had witnessed its population increase from just over 70,000 in 1801 to 525,000 by 1901. In the same period the population of Leeds grew from 53,000 to 430,000 **[110]**. It became a city in 1893, along with Sheffield and Glasgow. By then, nearly 26,000 people in the former were employed making cutlery, files, saws, etc whilst in Scotland's latest city, almost 30,000 of its population worked in the coalmining industry, with another 15,000 men in engineering-related jobs. In 1899 it was calculated that the 50 shipbuilding yards in the port and on the River Clyde had turned out 480,000 tons of steamships that year, just under half the total for the whole of Britain.

[107]
Severn Bridge
W. Key
watercolour
AE185.153 (detail)

Two long bridges were opened across two of Britain's river estuaries within a year of each other — the Tay Bridge opening in 1878 at 3.5km (11,600ft) in length, followed a year later by the 1,268m (4,161ft)-long Severn Bridge. Although the original Tay Bridge was quickly lost, that across the Severn Estuary remained in use until 1960.

[108]
Forth Railway Bridge
Under Construction
photograph, 1888
AE185.284

[109]
Nottingham Station
lithograph
George Hawkins (1810–52)
after A. Parker
published by Day & Haghe,
London, 1839
AE185.272 (detail)

The position of the new Midland
Counties Railway station outside
the town's boundaries, meant
Nottingham Council had to built
a new road and bridge over the
Nottingham Canal to connect
it to the settlement, neither
of which were ready for the
official opening of the railway
on 29 May 1839.

[110]
Western Panoramic View
of Leeds
engraving
James Baylis Allen (1803–76)
after Joseph Rhodes
(1782–1854)
published by Charles Fowler,
Leeds, 1832
AE185.423

A landscape already dominated
by textile mills and smoking
chimneys.

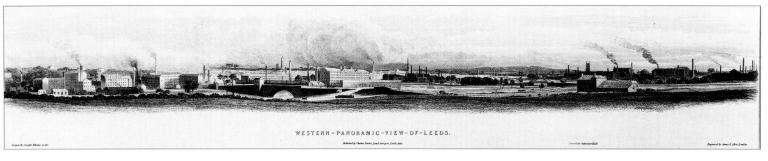

WESTERN-PANORAMIC-VIEW-OF-LEEDS.

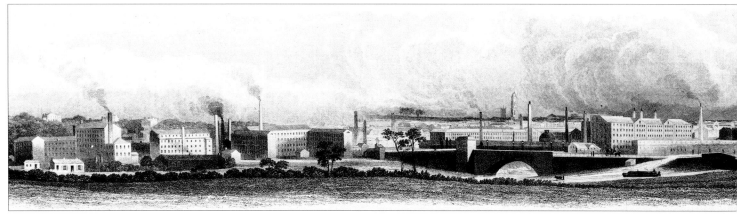

# Inland Navigation

Long before the Industrial Revolution, rivers had become the natural communication corridors of Britain. Over the years man-made channels were cut to enhance navigation and drainage and by the end of the 17th century there were a number of Acts of Parliament in place for the further improvement of rivers. Nevertheless, in this period nothing matched the 150-mile-long artificial waterway, the Canal du Midi in France, completed in 1681 to connect the Mediterranean to the Atlantic; it was many years before canals in Britain reached this mileage, and then it was mainly through piecemeal construction and gradual interlinking. The 10-mile-long Sankey Canal which opened in 1757 was the first substantial undertaking but it was quickly followed by a far more significant and influential feat of engineering, the Bridgewater Canal, linking the coalmines of Worsley to Manchester [111]. When a new connection between this canal was made to the Mersey at Runcorn a few years later, it encouraged the promotion of two further stretches of canal, the Trent & Mersey [112] and the Staffordshire & Worcestershire, which when fully completed in 1777 provided a continuous through route right across the industrial heart of the country from the Humber Estuary in the east to the mouth of the River Severn in the west. At numerous places along their courses these canals encouraged the expansion of existing or the establishment of new industries and settlements. Wedgwood's Etruria factory which has already been mentioned was an example of a new industrial development, whilst Stourport was a completely new town created where the Staffordshire & Worcestershire Canal joined the River Severn.

Birmingham and the Black Country prospered by their connections to this network of canals which was finally linked to the Thames via Oxford in 1789. The annual dividend returns were so good that investors clamoured to promote new routes in what was dubbed the 'Canal Mania'. Between 1791 and 1796 over 100 schemes went before Parliament, 51 gaining the Royal Assent. The new canals were more purposeful and heavily engineered [113] than their predecessors which, by hugging the natural contours of the land, had meandered around the countryside. In 1810 a through route from the Thames to Bristol was created when the Kennet & Avon Canal opened and by the second decade of the 19th century the Midlands system had better access to the capital via the Grand Junction with its connection to the Grand Union from Leicester. In the same period the Pennines were crossed, linking Hull to Liverpool, so that by the dawn of the railway age all the major centres of production and consumption from Lancashire and Yorkshire through the Midlands to London were interconnected by a network of canals [114].

[112]
Harecastle Tunnel,
Trent & Mersey Canal
etching, c1780
AE185.843

**[111]**
Bridgewater Canal
— The Aqueduct
aquatint
Merigot after J. C. Nattes
(c1765–1822)
AE185.608

This structure caused great excitement when it was completed in 1761 because it carried one stretch of water — the Bridgewater Canal — over another — the River Irwell. Although Roman engineers had achieved the same result with greater structures on the Continent, the Barton Aqueduct was just one example of what could be achieved in the new rational and technological society beginning to emerge in Britain in the 18th century.

**[113]** opposite
Lune Aqueduct
watercolour, c1798
Gideon Yates (fl 1798–1837)
AE185.170

From this view it is not clear that Lune Aqueduct was actually 183m (600ft) long, and made up of five arches. It was designed and built by John Rennie (1761–1821), with details by the architect Alexander Stevens (1730–96), as part of the Lancaster Canal, and completed in 1797. The town of Lancaster is visible through the arch.

**[114]**
The Double Lock and East
Entrance to the Islington
Tunnel, Regent's Canal
engraving
F. J. Havell after Thomas
H. Shepherd
published by Jones & Co,
London, 25 August 1827
AE185.598

The Regent's Canal was only 8½
miles long, but when completed in
1820 it provided an important link
between the Grand Junction Canal,
from the Midlands, and the London
Docks at Limehouse.

# Steam

There is no doubt that the steam engine in all its various forms has become synonymous with the Industrial Revolution. But it would be inaccurate to state that the steam engine powered that revolution from start to finish. For almost the whole of the 18th century, when innovation and creativity transformed Britain into the first industrialised nation in the world, water was the main source of power. The majority of textile mills, for example, remained completely reliant on waterwheels to run their equipment until well into the Victorian era. It was not until the end of the 19th century that steam eclipsed all other forms of power generation.

Thomas Newcomen (1663–1729) was the first man to develop a steam engine that could be put to practical use and its introduction in the first decades of the 18th century was a vital catalyst in the industrialisation process. The engines provided a continuous source of power which was not dependent on natural forces or the labours of humans and animals. They were the first reliable machines capable of draining water from underground workings to allow miners to search ever deeper for coal, copper, tin and other minerals. They were also installed to recycle water at sites that used waterwheels to drive bellows at blast furnaces or trip hammers at forges. Without their introduction further industrial development would have been severely curtailed.

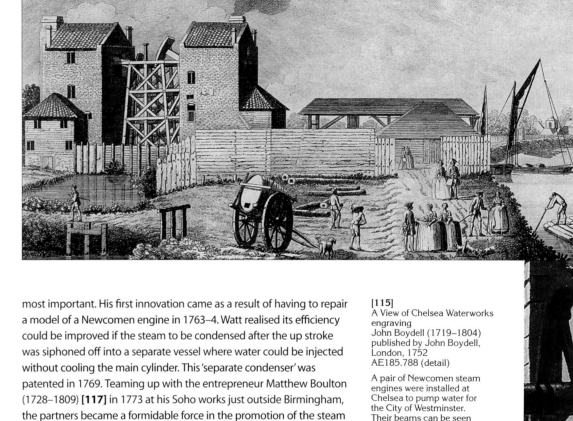

Newcomen experimented for many years before he had a robust machine capable of doing any useful work. The first engine was set up in the Black Country in 1712 to drain water from a coalmine in Tipton. Other industrialists were persuaded to install similar engines so that by the 1770s it has been estimated that just over 300 Newcomen atmospheric steam engines were in operation, the majority in the mines of Cornwall and the North East [115]. In that period, the fundamental design remained unchanged, the only alterations of any significance being the substitution of cast-iron in place of brass as the material for the cylinders and an increase in their diameter to try and produce more power. The ironworks in Shropshire became one of the main suppliers of cast-iron cylinders (see p12).

Though many engineers worked to try to improve the efficiency of the steam engine after Newcomen's death, the developments wrought by the Scottish instrument-maker James Watt (1736–1819) [116] were the

most important. His first innovation came as a result of having to repair a model of a Newcomen engine in 1763–4. Watt realised its efficiency could be improved if the steam to be condensed after the up stroke was siphoned off into a separate vessel where water could be injected without cooling the main cylinder. This 'separate condenser' was patented in 1769. Teaming up with the entrepreneur Matthew Boulton (1728–1809) [117] in 1773 at his Soho works just outside Birmingham, the partners became a formidable force in the promotion of the steam engine. As well as the separate condenser, a patent was secured to cover the principle of 'double action', whereby steam was used to drive the piston alternately in both directions in a fully enclosed cylinder. The expansive power of steam was also patented, so that taken together, all these improvements could save two-thirds of the amount of fuel needed to run Newcomen's atmospheric engines. Boulton & Watt were respected and hated in equal measure because of these innovations

[115]
A View of Chelsea Waterworks
engraving
John Boydell (1719–1804)
published by John Boydell, London, 1752
AE185.788 (detail)

A pair of Newcomen steam engines were installed at Chelsea to pump water for the City of Westminster. Their beams can be seen poking out of the buildings in this scene.

and because they fiercely defended their patents. Profits came not just from supplying engines but from extracting royalties from other engineers who built engines with the same features. And those other engineers were as keen as Watt to innovate and make money from their own ideas. In 1780, for example, Birmingham engineer, James Pickard patented a simple crank arrangement that turned the steam engine's pumping action into rotary motion. This simple device meant engines could be adapted to wind minerals out of mines or run machinery which, by releasing factories from their dependency on water [118], meant they could be sited anywhere. The financial rewards from this increased demand for engines were considerable, and as Boulton & Watt did not want to miss this opportunity to profit, but did

not want to infringe their rival's patent either, Watt devised his 'sun and planet' gears to achieve the same rotary motion. The importance of rotary motion is attested by figures that show of the 496 engines built by the partners up to 1800, 308 had that feature. By the start of the 19th century, Boulton & Watt engines were not just pumping water from mine workings but driving machinery in textile mills, ironworks, breweries, potteries, brickworks and many other manufactories [119].

Watt's role in improving the steam engine is legendary, but the effect of his patents did slow its development, particularly in the last decade of the 18th century. To avoid paying royalties to Watt, William Symington (1764–1831), for example, built an atmospheric engine in

[118]
The Iron Forge between Dolgelli
and Barmouth in Merionethshire
aquatint
Paul Sandby (1725–1809)
published by Paul Sandby,
London, 1 September 1776
AE185.759

Waterwheels had driven
machinery for centuries before
the Industrial Revolution. This
example powering a Welsh forge
was typical of hundreds to be
found wherever there was a
sufficient head of water.

[119]
A Steam Engine of 20 Horse
Power Constructed by Fenton,
Murray & Wood of Leeds
pen and wash drawing, c1822
Joseph Clement (1779–1844)
AE185.167

This image was engraved and
published in a number of books
about the steam engine, the first
being Charles Frederick
Partington's An Historical &
Descriptive Account of the
Steam Engine, 1822.

[120]
Middleton Colliery Railway
engraving, 1816
J. Pass
AE185.339 (detail)

In 1808 the owner of Middleton Colliery, J. C. Brandling, saw Trevithick's Catch Me Who Can locomotive at Euston, and discussed this with his manager, John Blenkinsop (1783–1831). In 1811 Blenkinsop patented his rack railway system, and Matthew Murray (1765–1826) built two locomotives to run on it, the first tried out in June 1812.

1788 to power Patrick Miller's (1731–1815) steam boat, over 20 years after Watt's inventions had rendered that type of engine obsolete. At this time there were other talented engineers who wanted to harness the power of high-pressure steam but were discouraged because of Watt's reputation for tenaciously pursuing those who he believed, rightly or wrongly, infringed his patent. There was no better proof of the brake Watt had put on innovation than the appearance of a number of fully functional high-pressure engines in the first five years following the expiration of his patent in 1800.

The man responsible for most of these was Richard Trevithick (1771–1833). It was this fiery Cornishman who successfully transformed the stationary beam engine into a motive power unit. He did this by developing a boiler that could sustain an internal pressure of up to 50psi to supply steam to a cylinder which, instead of exhausting that steam after each stroke of the piston into a separate condenser, that had been Watt's break-through invention, sent it into the boiler's chimney instead, helping to draw more air over the fire to raise its temperature and produce more steam. Trevithick's 'puffers', so called because of the sound made by the exhausting steam, were used in a number of locations. Once he had demonstrated that this arrangement

of using 'strong steam' was (comparatively) safe, it was inevitable that his inventive mind should turn to mounting his new compact engine on a vehicle so that it could be made to 'move under its own steam'. He was not the first to try (Nicolas Joseph Cugnot in 1769 and William Murdoch in 1784 had both built steam carriages) but Trevithick was the first to have a lasting influence on the work of others, most notably Matthew Murray (1765-1826) [120], William Hedley (1779–1843) [121] and George Stephenson (1781–1848).

In 1801 Trevithick successfully drove a steam-powered carriage on the roads of Camborne, Cornwall [122]. Pleased with this achievement, he celebrated with friends in a local hostelry, whilst unbeknown to the party the carriage caught fire and was completely destroyed. The following year, he was busy with plans for a replacement and for another engine that would operate on the 'real roads' of Coalbrookdale. Both engines were completed in 1803, the road carriage demonstrated to a large cheering crowd on Oxford Street in London, the plateway locomotive 140 miles away in Shropshire, destined to be forgotten and overlooked by generations of railway historians. Trevithick's Penydarren locomotive which followed in 1804 was not forgotten and has justifiably been celebrated as the first successful steam locomotive [123].

[121]
Puffing Billy
photograph, c1863
AE185.319

This locomotive was originally
built by William Hedley
(1779–1843) for use at Wylam
Colliery, Northumberland, after
Richard Trevithick had refused
to supply one of his own design.
Hedley's engine was modified
over the years, and this
photograph shows it in the state
it was when presented to the
South Kensington Museum
in 1863.

[123]  opposite
Quaker's Yard Viaduct
watercolour, 1841
(attrib) Penry Williams
(1798–1885)
AE185.165

In the foreground of this picture
is the Penydarren Tramroad,
opened in 1802 to connect
the ironworks at Merthyr Tydfil
to the Glamorganshire Canal
10 miles away at Abercynon.
It was on this tramroad that
Trevithick's second steam
locomotive was successfully
run in February 1804.

PAT'S COMMENT ON STEAM ENGINES.

*By-and-bye a Man will go a hunting after breakfast upon his Tay-kettle.*

[122]
Pat's Comment on
Steam Engines
etching
'A. Sharpshooter'
published by G. Humphrey,
London, 28 August 1829
AE185.372

Other engineers did follow
Trevithick in building successful
road carriages in the 1820s and
1830s, but no one was able to
supplant the horse for personal
use as suggested in this print.

Trevithick did not develop the locomotive any further, and it was left to others, most notably George and Robert Stephenson, to demonstrate its true potential. *Rocket's* triumph at the Rainhill Trials of 1829 ensured the Liverpool & Manchester Railway was the first line anywhere in the world to be operated entirely by steam locomotives, setting the standards for all subsequent railways. As they spread throughout the country and abroad, stationary engines also became more efficient and powerful. Engines without beams using the same direct drive action as steam locomotives — ie piston connected to crank and wheel — soon followed and as the 19th century progressed they became ever more sophisticated, efficient and powerful. Machines with single cylinders were the most common form of these horizontal engines but as manufacturing and assembly tolerances improved, variants were built with up to four cylinders to make the most of the expansive properties of steam before it was expelled into the atmosphere. Horizontal compound engines became particularly popular in textile mills, with the vertical equivalents finding favour in steamships.

The development and use of the steam engine, both stationary and locomotive, was a turning point in the way manufacturers and transport providers considered their work. The steam engine was the first practical device that could supplant wind, water, animal and human power. For the first time, industrialists were able to concentrate their efforts on the machinery making the product, manipulating the material or providing the passengers with the means to get from one place to another. Manufacturers could focus on improving the machinery of production without having to take into account whether or not there would be enough water to turn the wheel to drive that machinery, or whether or not the wind would blow, or how long the horse could turn the gin until it became too tired or needed to stop to be fed and watered. The steam engine was not affected by the weather or the seasons. It never got tired and, properly maintained, with enough steam to feed the cylinders, it could provide a continuous output of power. It allowed entrepreneurs and industrialists to deal with the ends rather than the means. This was the most fundamental legacy of the steam engine for the modern world. It created a way of thinking that meant later generations were not concerned about electric motors, the internal combustion engine or batteries, *per se*, only that their washing machines, cars or mobile phones did what they were supposed to do.

# Railways

Train of Waggons crossing the Turnpike Road near Darlington.

[124]
View of the opening of the
Stockton & Darlington Railway
lithograph, c1825
J. Bousefield
AE185.327 (detail)

One of three views which were
included on the same sheet,
this shows a 'Train of Waggons
crossing the Turnpike Road near
Darlington' on 27 September
1825, the opening day of the
Stockton & Darlington Railway.

The railways of Great Britain have generated more interest that any other industrial activity in this country, and this is mirrored in the Elton Collection which has an undoubted bias towards railway material. The collection contains more books and images on the subject than any other. Like so many boys of his generation, Elton's interest in industry, engineering and topography grew out of his boyhood enthusiasm for railways. It was part of his education long before 'train spotting' became a derogatory term.

As mentioned in Chapter One, the 'railway age' can be considered the culmination of the Industrial Revolution. What it did was put a communication system into place which allowed the full potential of all the innovations of the 18th century to be realised. The foundations of Britain's railway system were laid between 1825 and 1851, and by the end of the century the network was as good as complete. It was created principally as the result of three economic imperatives. The first was a need to break the monopoly of the canal companies

who had become the only viable carriers for goods overland. This was combined with a growing belief that railways could genuinely improve communication between the suppliers of raw materials, the producers of finished products and their respective markets. It was these forces which led to the construction and opening of the Stockton & Darlington Railway in 1825 **[124]**, and prompted the first wave of railway promotion. The final imperative (which is the natural ingredient of any capitalist society) was the need to find new ways of making money. After the astonishing success of the Liverpool & Manchester Railway as a passenger-carrying line in the first years of the 1830s, the ownership of railway shares seemed to offer opportunities for lucrative returns. Another period of railway development followed which witnessed the building of such trunk railways as the London & Birmingham **[125]**, the Grand Junction (between Birmingham and the Liverpool & Manchester Railway at Warrington), the Great Western (between London and Bristol), the London & Southampton **[126],** the London & Brighton **[127]**, and the

[125]
Blisworth Cutting
watercolour, 1849
F. Swanson
AE185.23

The London & Birmingham Railway
was opened throughout in September
1838 and incorporated some
impressive engineering features,
including this dramatic rock cutting
outside Blisworth in Northamptonshire.

[126]
Southampton Station
engraving
published by
J. & F. Harwood, 1841
AE185.715

The London & Southampton Railway
was opened in stages between May
1838 and June 1839, when the final
stretch from Winchester to Southampton
was brought into use. This is a view
of the original terminal building at
Southampton designed by Sir William
Tite (1798–1873).

## Railway Companies Represented by Paintings, Drawings and/or Prints in the Elton Collection

Aberdeen & Inverness Junction Railway

Birmingham & Gloucester Railway

Bishop's Castle Railway

Bodmin & Wadebridge Railway

Bristol & Exeter Railway

Canterbury & Whitstable Railway

Chester & Crewe Railway

Chester & Holyhead Railway

Cornwall Railway

Drumburgh & Port Carlisle Railway

East & West Yorkshire Junction Railway

East London Railway

Eastern Counties Railway

Eastern Union Railway

Edinburgh & Glasgow Railway

Glasgow & Paisley Railway

Grand Junction Railway

Great Eastern Railway

Great North of England Railway

Great Northern Railway

Great Southern & Western Railway

Great Western Railway

Huddersfield & Sheffield Junction Railway

Hull & Selby Railway

Kent Railway

Lancashire & Yorkshire Railway

Leeds & Thirsk Railway

Liverpool & Manchester Railway

London & Birmingham Railway

London & Blackwall Railway

London, Brighton & South Coast Railway

London, Chatham & Dover Railway

London & Croydon Railway

London & Greenwich Railway

London & North Western Railway

London & South Western Railway

London & Southampton Railway

Metropolitan Railway

Midland Railway

Midland Counties Railway

Newcastle & Carlisle Railway

Newcastle, North Shields & Tynemouth Railway

Norfolk Railway

North British Railway

North Eastern Railway

North London Railway

Oxford, Worcester & Wolverhampton Railway

Paisley & Renfrew Railway

Reading, Guildford & Reigate Railway

Severn Bridge Railway

Severn & Wye Railway

Shrewsbury & Birmingham Railway

Shrewsbury & Chester Railway

South Devon Railway

South Eastern Railway

South Staffordshire Railway

South Wales Railway

Stockton & Darlington Railway

Taff Vale Railway

Tilbury & Gravesend Tunnel Junction Railway

West Midland Railway

Westminster Bridge, Deptford & Greenwich Railway

Whitby & Pickering Railway

York & North Midland Railway

[127]
Haywards Heath Tunnel
(South End)
watercolour, 1842
AE185.27

The London & Brighton Railway
was opened as far as Haywards
Heath on 12 July 1841, from
where passengers continued
their journey to the South Coast
by road coaches. The line
through this tunnel and onwards
to Brighton finally opened on
21 September that year.

[128]
Facts & Fancies No 9
lithograph, hand-coloured
published by W. Spooner, c1845
AE185.507

A small boy returns some
washing to a stout woman,
requesting to be paid at once
because his mother is going to
sell the mangle to buy railway
shares.

WAITING FOR "THE RAILWAY TIMES."

(AFTER HAYDON.)

Manchester & Birmingham, to name but a few. Within a few years of these lines becoming fully operational, the whole country was gripped by another wave of speculation, but more intensive than ever before. The 'Railway Mania' of 1845–6 truly became a frenzied rush to 'get rich quick'. Between 1845 and 1848 almost 650 Acts of Parliament were passed for new lines out of hundreds more that failed at the committee stages. A few of the latter were sound undertakings, but the majority of schemes were purely speculative ventures into which all classes of society sank millions of pounds, both in actual money and promissory 'scrip' **[128]**. Some fortunes were made, but thousands of people saw no return for their investment **[129]**.

The Elton Collection is particularly strong in material from the 'Railway Mania' period, and has an unrivalled selection of images of railways opened between the 1830s and 1850s. A list of railway companies of which there are paintings, drawings and/or prints is the best way of indicating how extensive this part of the collection is (see adjacent table). The images are predominantly of railways in the landscape, sometimes with the civil engineering and architecture to the fore. There are also some beautiful prints of railway station buildings both large and small **[130, 131** and **132]**. There are not so many views of individual locomotives, only a handful that might be considered

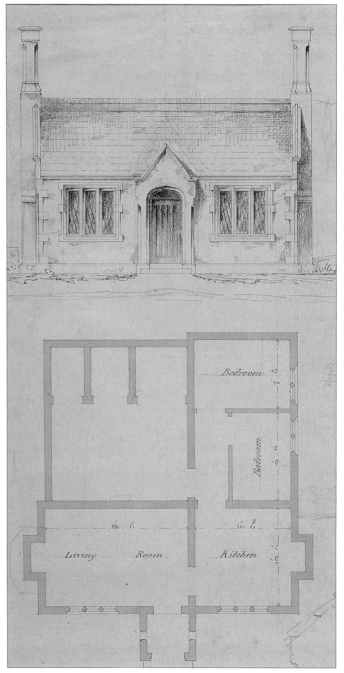

**[129]**
Waiting for The Railway Times
wash drawing, 1845
John Leech (1817–1864)
AE185.82

Leech provided over 3,000 cartoons for the periodical Punch, and this was one. Published at the height of the 'Railway Mania', it was a parody of a well-known painting by Benjamin Haydon (1786–1846), 'Waiting for the Times'. The Railway Times had a short life, but flourished as a means of advertising all the latest railway projects until the end of the decade.

**[130]**
Design for Railway Cottage; Elevation and Plan
pen and wash drawing
J. A. Davies
AE185.105

Not all railway buildings were designed by professional architects, but if they were, this style, often referred to as 'cottage orné', was a favourite choice for crossing keepers' cottages in the 1840s.

[131]
Brighton Station
lithograph, tinted, 1841
G. Childs (fl 1826–73) after
David Mocatta (1806–82)
AE185.253

For larger stations, the preferred
style in the 1830s and 1840s
was a classical one, and that
was the choice of the architect,
David Mocatta, for Brighton
station.

railway engineering drawings [133], and hardly any pictures of
signalboxes [134], unknown until the mid-1850s. By then, when
railways had become an accepted part of the landscape, there were
altogether fewer images, and the collection reflects this [135]. The
popularity of railway subjects emerged again only a generation later
but in a completely different form. At the end of the 19th century
commercial and amateur photographers turned their attention to the
railway companies' immaculately maintained steam locomotives and
trains to the exclusion of almost all other aspects of railway operation.
Elton's collection of postcard views of engines, a collection started as a

boy, reflects that renewed and specialist interest [136]. Unlike the mid-
century railway views produced for print collectors and bibliophiles,
the new range of sepia or coloured postcards was aimed squarely at
a new 'railway enthusiast' market which included young men such as
Elton, John Betjeman and the prolific author O. S. Nock. Although
Elton's collection of commercially produced railway postcards is by no
means unique, and not of great historical significance when compared
with other material he collected, it does give us an insight into the man
as an enthusiast as well as being a tangible reminder of what kindled
his initial interest in industrial subjects.

[132]
Oxford, Bird's-eye View
of the Proposed Station
lithograph, hand-coloured
T. Picken (fl 1838-70)
published by Day & Son
AE185.803

The Oxford, Worcester &
Wolverhampton Railway,
authorised in 1845, was not
completed until 1854, and
then not as originally planned.
This was the lavish station the
company proposed for Oxford
but never built.

**[133]**
Chester
wash drawing, c1850
AE185.66

This side elevation of an 0-6-0
goods locomotive (a product
of Benjamin Hick & Son Ltd of
Bolton), shows that engineering
drawings of this period were
closer to 'artists' impressions'
than simple scaled diagrams.

N.B. Railway.—Express leaving Edinburgh.

[137]
Dowlais Rolling Mills
wash drawing, c1890
C. W. Campion
AE185.120

The artist obviously witnessed the rolling of wrought-iron for himself, and made this sketch either on the spot or shortly after his experience. The figures are shown pulling hot iron bars through the grooves in the rollers. Once through, the bars would have been passed over the top of the rollers, inserted into a smaller groove and pulled through again, each pass reducing the thickness of the bars until the required section was achieved.

# Mining and Heavy Industry

As outlined in the topography section of this chapter, mining and heavy industry made an increasing impact on the landscape from the middle of the 18th century. The drama of ironworks was particularly alluring to artists. Coalbrookdale was one of the first places on their itinerary in the 18th century, followed by South Wales **[137]** and the North East in the 19th century **[138]**. Of all the views of ironworks painted by professional artists, however, very few were completed by men who had actually worked in the surroundings depicted. The exception was James Sharples (1825–92). In the mid-1840s he was a practising artist, but was entirely self-taught, both in artistic technique and basic reading and writing, and had gained those skills whilst an apprentice at the Phoenix Foundry in Bury, Lancashire. It was in the very little spare time he had that he completed a large canvas entitled 'The Forge'. The scene was typical of foundries all over the country with all the necessary paraphernalia accurately reproduced. But Sharples' figures, some drawn from friends in the foundry, struck heroic poses as if they were characters from the ancient world. And the whole canvas had an extra heroic dimension because those figures had been painted by one of their own. By the time the painting was completed in 1847, Sharples was earning a precarious living as a portrait painter, but he soon returned to 'The Forge' and spent the whole of the 1850s making an engraving of the scene **[139]**. The resultant prints were both a critical and popular success, and although they never repaid the effort expended on making the plate, the endeavour did ensure Sharples' reputation when his story was retold by Samuel Smiles in his book, *Self-Help*. Another reward was to be given the commission in 1851 to design one of the first trade union emblems, for the Amalgamated Society of Engineers **[140]**.

Away from the coalmines and ironworks, the environments created by the extraction of stone **[141]**, clay, copper, lead and tin were just as inspirational for 18th and early 19th-century artists. Such was the notoriety of Parys Mountain on Anglesey **[142]**, the richest source of copper in Britain, for example, that it outstripped any other industrial site as a visitor attraction by the end of the 18th century. The deposits had been discovered only a few decades earlier, and the ore was eventually both quarried and mined from almost 150 shafts.

Exploitation quickly made a lunar landscape of the area and Henry Skrine, who visited in 1798 and witnessed the effects of the calcining kilns, described the site as: '. . . a large arid mountain, entirely stripped of its herbage by the steam of the sulphur works . . .'. The output of Parys Mountain had depressed the older copper industry in Cornwall which then had to rely on tin mining and China clay extraction, but these wild Cornish settings soon encouraged artists to venture to this remote county, the workings at Carclase, St Austell, for example, attracting Royal Academician, Joseph Farington (1747–1821) **[143]**.

[138]
Tapping the Furnaces
wash drawing, c1865
Alfred William Hunt (1830–96)
AE185.121

This image was a preliminary sketch for an oil painting currently in the Tate Gallery collection. It dramatically shows the moment when molten iron was allowed to flow out of the blast furnaces in a Middlesbrough ironworks, a scene repeated thousands of times in 18th and 19th-century ironworks all over Britain.

[139]
The Forge
engraving, 1859
James Sharples (1825–92)
AE185.768 (detail)

[140]
The Amalgamated Society
of Engineers' Membership
Certificate
engraving
William Greatbach (b 1802)
after James Sharples
(1825–92)
published by Blades & East,
1852
AE185.786

[141]
Bathstone Quarries
aquatint, hand-coloured
John Hassell
published by F. Jukes,
London, 31 March 1798
AE185.454

The methods of quarrying
stone had changed very
little for centuries, as this
late 18th-century print
shows.

[142]
The Parys Mine
wash drawing
John Samuel Hayward
(1778-1822)
AE185.119

[143]
Carclase Tin Mine
pencil drawing
Joseph Farington (1747–1821)
AE185.112

Farington's pencil sketches
were always meticulous and
accurate records of the scene
before him, the two he produced
of Coalbrookdale and Ironbridge
in 1789, for example, being of
enormous use to current
industrial archaeologists.

# The Great Exhibition

The year 1851 was more than the chronological fulcrum of the 19th century. For historians it has become a watershed in the transformation of Britain from an agrarian society to an industrial one. But its significance could also be detected at the time and it marked not just an economic turning point [144].

Britain had become the country of 'dark satanic mills' in the years between 1800 and 1851, in which working conditions for millions were appalling. The industrial towns had become overcrowded, with speculative housing developed to accommodate as many people as possible [145]. Sanitation was poor, and in the 1830s cholera became the plague of the industrial age. Life expectancy was short and mortality amongst children was high. Most factory workers could not read or write, and fewer still had any influence on the way the country was governed. The Chartists uprisings in the 1830s followed by the 'hungry forties' might have led to revolutions like those experienced in Europe in 1848 if it had not been for a genuine belief that change was possible. When Friedrich Engels published *The Condition of the Working Classes in England* in 1845 there was already a latent desire for reform. In 1842, Parliament had been shocked at the findings of the Select Committee on the Employment of Women & Children in Mines and the report on the sanitary condition of the labouring population. Four years later the Corn Laws were repealed, ostensibly to alleviate poverty, and this was quickly followed by the very first piece of legislation to control the hours of paid employment — the Ten Hours Act.

This desire for change was, paradoxically, also the desire for social stability. After 1851 living standards for many, particularly the new middle classes, did improve. It has been calculated that by the end of the 19th century, on average real income per head of the population had increased four-fold. The expanding railway network made it easier to move around the country in search of work, and when employment was found, as it was more often than not secured for life, there were few reasons for upsetting the *status quo* by direct action. At the same time there was a growing awareness of, and pride in, nationality, fuelled by a steady expansion and consolidation of the British Empire. Nineteenth-century British nationalism was based on superiority which helped give all sections of society a common purpose. Nowhere was this unifying pride better demonstrated than in the Great Exhibition of 1851 [146].

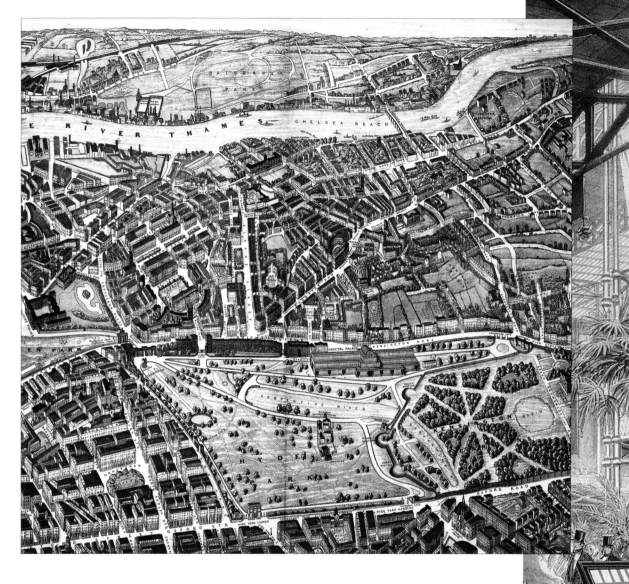

[144]
A Balloon View of London
engraving
published by Banks & Co, London,
1 May 1851
AE185.5026 (detail)

Unlike most maps, this fascinating view looked at the capital from north to south. It is an important record of the largest city in Britain in the first year that the majority of the country's population lived in urban centres

140

PRINTED & PUBLISHED BY STANNARD & DIXON, 7, POLAND ST.

**[147 and 148]**
London in 1851; Manchester in 1851
etchings
George Cruikshank
(1792–1878)
published by D. Bogue, London, 1851
AE185.492.9 and .10

The railways played a large part in the success of the Great Exhibition by providing the means of transporting thousands of people from all over the country to the capital. Hundreds of special excursions were run with overnight accommodation advertised as part of the package. These two images were part of a set of 11 issued by Cruikshank to celebrate the Exhibition.

As the industrial towns of central and northern England emptied into the railway excursions to the capital, there was no violent revolution as Europe had witnessed only three years before **[147** and **148]**. The Crystal Palace became for a few months the cathedral for the new all-embracing national religion. And in that cathedral worker and master stood peacefully and proudly side by side to sing the praises of the fruits of their collective labours, marvelling — in a superior way — at the products of lesser nations. British goods were icons of a rational, scientific and modern society **[149]**, contrasting directly with the exotic fripperies of other less civilised societies **[150]**. The achievement of the Great Exhibition in binding the nation together in a common purpose was as impressive as the physical structure of the Crystal Palace that housed the displays.

[149]
The Transept
From Dickinson's
Comprehensive Picture of the
Great Exhibition of 1851, Vol II
chromolithograph
AE185.5284

[150] opposite
The Turkey Stand
From Recollections of the
Great Exhibition, 1851
Day & Sons, 1851
chromolithograph
AE185.5286

# Thames Tunnel

The building of the first tunnel under a river was truly an instance when fact was stranger than fiction. What might have been a simple story of a subterranean passage became an epic tale of danger, heroic deeds, death and dogged perseverance. What was planned to take three years to complete, in fact took 19. When work started on the Thames Tunnel in 1824, the Stockton & Darlington Railway was yet to open and the horse was still the undisputed motive power for all land transport. By the time the tunnel was completed in 1843, steam locomotives were travelling up and down the Great Western Railway between London and Bristol at over 50mph on a route laid out by the tunnel engineer's son, Isambard Kingdom Brunel.

Cornish engineer Robert Vazie was the first man known to have tried to tunnel under the River Thames. Within months of work starting in 1806, he was joined by fellow Cornishman, Richard Trevithick. The two men worked for the Thames Archway Company on an equal footing until Trevithick was given sole charge in the autumn of 1807. When the river broke into the workings at the end of January the following year, however, Vazie and his supporters accused Trevithick of incompetence and all work stopped, never to be resumed again. Trevithick made a number of proposals for continuing the work, including building the tunnel from cast-iron sections bolted together to form a continuous tube (a technique eventually used to create the deep underground rail network beneath the capital in the 20th century), but no one had the will to proceed, so the endeavour was abandoned.

Barely 10 years later, however, a tunnelling device patented by Marc Isambard Brunel in January 1818, raised new hopes. Brunel's inspiration is said to have come from observing how the ship worm 'teredo navalis' bored through wooden hulls beneath the protection of a fine shell. The human equivalent was to be a cast-iron shield which protected a group of miners whilst they worked. When sufficient spoil had been removed, the shield was pushed forward and brickwork inserted behind the miners. Ingenious though Brunel's device was, it was not put to use immediately, and six years elapsed before the Thames Tunnel Company received Parliamentary approval to construct a tunnel between Rotherhithe and Wapping. When the shaft at the former was completed in November 1825, work started on installing the shield. As the tunnel was to have two parallel roadways, it differed

[151] opposite
Banquet in the Thames Tunnel
oil on board
attrib George Jones
(1786–1869)
AE185.157

Although Marc Brunel was not present at the banquet, the artist included him to the left of the painting, instantly recognisable by his spectacles.

[152]
The Thames Tunnel
aquatint, hand-coloured,
9 November 1830
published by R. H. Laurie,
London, 9 November 1830
AE185.622 (detail)

When this print was issued, work on the tunnel had been suspended for almost three years and was destined not to start again for another five. The print was one of a number sold to try and raise funds to continue the work.

from Brunel's original patent by being rectangular rather than circular in section. It comprised 12 compartments, each three cells high, allowing one man to work in each cell.

Marc's son, Isambard Kingdom Brunel, was promoted from assisting his father on site to resident engineer at the start of 1827 after William Armstrong, who had held that post originally, suffered a breakdown due to the stress of the work. The younger Brunel's energy became legendary. He lived on site, working for 12 hours a day like the rest of the men, and then going without sleep by planning through the night. By March 1827 he had over 450 men tunnelling beneath the Thames, and two months later the centre of the river was about to be reached. Then the problems began. One of the assistant engineers died as a direct result of the poor conditions underground, and on 18 May the tunnel was completely flooded when the ground above the shield gave way. The young Brunel and his assistant William Gravatt helped all the workers to safety. When digging restarted, the Tunnel Company decided to celebrate by holding an event in the workings on 10 November 1827 for 150 of its workforce

whilst, at a discreet distance, laying on a banquet for 50 invited guests [151]. The gesture could have been a catastrophe, because in early January the following year the Thames broke into the workings so quickly that six workers were killed and Brunel himself narrowly avoided being drowned. His injuries and the effects to his general health were severe and he never worked on the tunnel project again.

Tunnelling did not resume until 1835, as before under Marc Brunel's supervision, but with a considerable £270,000 loan from the Treasury. Progress was painfully slow, the whole enterprise driven more by the will not to be defeated than by any real need for completion. For his perseverance, Brunel was awarded a knighthood in 1841. Plans for graded approaches on either side of the river which would have allowed wheeled vehicles to use the tunnel were abandoned, which meant that when it was finally completed and opened in March 1843, it could be used only by pedestrians [152]. Eventually the tunnel became part of the London underground railway network in 1865 when the East London Railway incorporated it into its system.

# Ships and Shipping

Shipbuilding, like so many traditional craft skills that had remained fundamentally unchanged for generations, became a very different profession as a result of the Industrial Revolution. The innovations which most affected it were steam engines and rolled iron plates, although these did not change the course of design overnight. The earliest serious proposals for using steam engines as a means of propulsion can be traced back to the late 17th century, whilst 1777 is the accepted date for the earliest boat with an iron hull. But neither the use of steam engines nor iron construction completely supplanted the traditional sailing ship until the beginning of the 20th century. The design of sailing ships with wooden hulls continued to improve, with increasing numbers built of greater size and efficiency before they were finally supplanted by steamships with metal hulls.

It may surprise many railway enthusiasts to learn that almost 20 years before Richard Trevithick's Penydarren locomotive made such an impact on railway history in 1804, steam engines had been successfully powering a number of boats in France, Britain and America. Probably the first steamboat of which there is indisputable evidence was built in France by the Marquis Claude de Jouffroy d'Abbans and launched in 1783. The 'Pyroscaphe' was a big vessel at 46m (150ft) long. Between 1785 and 1796 the American John Fitch (1743–98) constructed four vessels, the first successful trial being on 22 August 1787 on the River Delaware. Fitch's arch rival at the time was James Rumsey (1743-92), who carried out trials on the Potomac River with a boat with an engine that sucked water from the river and then pumped it out of the stern to propel the vessel forward. In 1788 he travelled to Britain where work was started on a boat with his design of engine. Unfortunately, he died before its successful trial on the River Thames in 1793.

By coincidence, in the same year Rumsey came to London, the first steam-powered British-designed boat had been sailed on Dalswinton Loch in Dumfriesshire in October 1788. The vessel had two hulls, one for the engine, the other for the boiler. Patrick Miller (1731–1815), who had been experimenting with human-powered paddle wheels on boats, had persuaded the young Scottish engineer William Symington (1764–1831) to provide him with a steam engine which could do the job instead. Symington went on to supply engines for a further three steam boats, the last two christened the *Charlotte*

*Dundas*. The second boat of that name, with an engine patented by Symington in October 1802, hauled a pair of sloops for almost 20 miles along the Forth & Clyde Canal to Glasgow, sailing against a considerable headwind on 28 March 1803, to prove the commercial possibilities of such vessels **[153]**.

The first commercial steamboat passenger service in Britain was operated by *Comet*, designed by Henry Bell (1767–1830) and launched in July 1812 **[154]**. This 12m (40ft)-long boat plied between Glasgow and Greenock on the River Clyde. By 1818 there were 18 steamboats working on that river, and in the years prior to reliable transportation by railways, passenger and goods-carrying steamboats began to operate on the rivers Trent, Mersey and Thames **[155]**. As an example of the

**[154]**
Steam Boat on the Clyde
near Dumbarton
aquatint, hand-coloured
William Daniell (1769–1837)
published by Longman & Co,
London, 1 February 1817
AE185.774 (detail)

A view of Henry Bell's Comet,
at work on the Clyde. As with
most other early steam boats,
Comet had a short life.
Launched on 24 July 1812, the
boat was wrecked beyond repair
in December 1820 on a journey
between Glasgow and Fort
William.

**[155]**
The London Engineer
aquatint, hand-coloured
published by R. Ackerman,
1819
AE185.464

This steam boat was built
in 1818 with paddle wheels
at the rear. It was used to run
a passenger service along the
River Thames and the Kent
coast between London and
Margate.

success of these services, it has been estimated that in 1836 almost 200,000 passengers a year travelled on the Forth & Clyde Canal.

The steamboat's transformation into the steamship soon followed. The first crossing of the Atlantic by steam (and sail) from America to Britain in 1819 was followed two years later by the first westbound crossing completed by the British steamship PS *Rising Star* (in the same year the very first steamboat with an iron hull was being fabricated at Tipton in the Black Country [PS *Aaron Manby*]). The pioneer who tried to turn steamships into what future generations would recognise as liners was Isambard Kingdom Brunel. He wanted to provide a higher standard of passenger comfort and much better facilities than were then available on existing ships. Like his advocacy of the 7ft gauge of track for the Great Western Railway, he wanted the rewards he believed only scale could deliver. The child of his imagination was the SS *Great Eastern*, a colossal ship by the standards of the day which cost him his health and nearly his reputation. But before that ship went into service, Brunel went through an intense and hurried apprenticeship.

As was to be expected of such a man, his apprentice pieces were very different from those of other young engineers. The PS *Great Western* was his first, built for the Great Western Steamship Co and launched in

1837. At 72m (236ft) long, the ship's avowed aim was to continue the journey of passengers travelling on the Great Western Railway between London and Bristol onwards to New York. That it achieved on 8 April 1838, arriving in America 15 days later with coal to spare. Not content with that performance, which was maintained regularly for the next eight years, Brunel's second vessel was 98m (322ft) long with an iron hull fitted out to accommodate 252 passengers and 130 crew. During her design the paddle wheels that had by then become standard for any reputable steamship were abandoned in favour of screw propulsion, proved to Brunel's satisfaction on the appropriately named SS *Archimedes* which had sailed into Bristol in May 1840 and been borrowed by the engineer for trials of his own. To drive Brunel's 4.7m (15ft 6in)-diameter screw propeller, his SS *Great Britain* was fitted with engines made to his father's patent of 1822. The vessel was completed at Bristol in 1843, but commenced her first transatlantic journey from Liverpool on 26 August 1845, completing the voyage to New York in 14 days, 21 hours [156]. Various modifications followed, including a replacement propeller and the removal of one of her masts, and for the next 35 years the ship made regular trips between Liverpool and Melbourne, Australia. Her exploits after that are too numerous to detail here; sufficient to record that in 1970 the hull was returned from the Falkland Islands to Bristol where restoration continues to this day.

The SS *Great Britain* was one of Brunel's greatest achievements and one for which there was a real commercial demand. The same could not be said of the SS *Great Eastern*, six times larger than any existing ship at approaching 19,000 tons, 211m (692ft) long, and with both paddle wheels and a screw propeller [157]. Work on this monster began in 1854 in the Millwall shipyard of Brunel's colleague John Scott Russell (1808–82). As there was no precedent for such a large undertaking, the two men were often in disagreement and their relationship deteriorated as work progressed. Nevertheless, by the autumn of 1857 the massive hull with the skeleton of the paddle wheels *in situ* was ready for launching. Built parallel to the River Thames, it was to be slid sideways into the water, but the first attempt on 3 November was abandoned after a winchman was killed. A second try on 31 January 1858 was successful. Fitting out took another 20 months, and then on 7 September 1859 the ship moved under its own steam for the first time down the Thames. Eight days later Brunel died of a stroke at the age of 53, his death hastened by his work on this huge project.

The subsequent history of the 'Leviathan', as the vessel was commonly known, was as depressing as the loss of Brunel. On its maiden voyage

[157]
Great Eastern Steam Ship
Medallion
AE185.1928

[158]
Daniel Gooch (1818–89)
photograph, 1845
AE185.566

A photograph of Gooch in his
late twenties standing proudly
next to a model of his 'Fire Fly'
class of 2-2-2 express
locomotives that was the first
to realise the full potential of
Brunel's broad gauge Great
Western Railway. Gooch made
his reputation as locomotive
superintendent for the company,
before resigning in 1864, only
to be brought back the following
year as the railway company's
new chairman.

in the English Channel five stokers were scalded to death after a violent explosion which ripped off one of the five funnels and a section of deck. The captain lost his life when being rowed to the ship in Southampton Water, and after only a comparatively short life carrying passengers across the Atlantic, the ship was put up for auction in 1863. With a touch of irony the successful bidder was Daniel Gooch (1816–89) who had worked closely with Brunel to ensure the Great Western Railway survived its formative years [158]. Gooch wanted the vessel for its size, large enough to carry the thick heavily insulated electric cable needed to replace the first, and short-lived, telegraph cable laid between Ireland and America in 1857–8. The SS *Great Eastern* was modified to carry the necessary 1,660 nautical miles of cable, and in June 1865, starting from the west coast of Ireland, began to lower the cable to the sea bed [159]. All went comparatively well until the ship was within sight of the Newfoundland coast and then the cable snapped. The project was abandoned for the season and it was not until July the following year that the missing section was spliced in, and the transatlantic telegraph brought back into operation. Gooch was made a baronet as a result, and the achievement marked the beginning of what would now be termed global communication, as disparate parts of the British Empire were progressively linked by cable. For the SS *Great Eastern*, however, it was its last adventure, and in 1888 the ship was dismantled.

# Portraits

The Elton Collection has a number of portraits of leading industrialists, engineers, railway managers and other personalities of the 18th and 19th centuries. The following is a list of that material.

Prince Albert, engraving, D. J. Pound after a photograph by J. E. Mayall (AE185.553)

Ralph Allen, aquatint, 1754, J. Faber after Thomas Hudson (AE185.554)

Matthew Boulton, pencil drawing (AE185.97)

James Brindley, engraving, H. Cook after F. Parsons (AE185.749)

Thomas Brown, engineer of the Ebbw Vale Railway, mezzotint, 1863, G. R. Ward (AE185.555)

Isambard Kingdom Brunel, engraving, D. J. Pound after a photograph by J. E. Mayall (AE185.556)

Isambard Kingdom Brunel, mezzotint, 1858, Henry Cousins after J. C. Horsley (AE185.557)

Isambard Kingdom Brunel, tinted lithograph, (F. W. Fairbrother, publisher) (AE185.558)

Marc Isambard Brunel, mezzotint, 1846, J. Carter after S. Drummond (AE185.559)

William James Chaplin, chairman of the London & South Western Railway, mezzotint, 1850, H. T. Ryall after F. Newenham (AE185.560)

Richard Creed, secretary of the London & Birmingham Railway, mezzotint, 1848, Edward McInnes after H. W. Phillips (AE185.561)

Samuel Crompton, inventor of the spinning machine called the 'Mule', mezzotint, S. W. Reynolds after Allingham (AE185.562)

Thomas Cubitt, architect, mezzotint, G. R. Ward after H. W. Pickersgill (AE185.563)

Sir William Cubitt, engineer, mezzotint, T. L. Atkinson after Sir Francis Grant (AE185.564)

Edmund Denison, chairman of the Great Northern Railway, mezzotint, 1848, S. W. Reynolds after H. W. Pickersgill (AE185.565)

Daniel Gooch, photograph (AE185.566)

John Hawkshaw, mezzotint, 1866, James Faed after James Edgell Collins (AE185.567)

George Hudson, the Railway King, tinted lithograph, 1845, Richard Doyle (attrib) (AE185.568)

William Huskisson MP, aquatint, 1832, Thomas Hodgetts after R. Rothwell (AE185.569)

William Huskisson MP, lithograph, 1830 (AE185.745)

Lord Kitchener, etching (AE185.2703)

Joseph Locke, engineer, mezzotint, 1849, Henry Cousins after Sir Francis Grant (AE185.570)

John Martin, photo-lithograph, 1854, James Akerman after Charles Martin (AE185.571)

Alexander Nasmyth, lithograph, (signed) (AE185.748)

Samuel Parkes, stipple engraving, 1822, George Parker after Abraham Wivell (AE185.747)

Sir Boverton Redwood, petroleum chemist, a *Vanity Fair* cartoon by 'Spy' (AE185.572)

John Rennie, engineer, mezzotint, S. W. Reynolds after a bust by Sir Francis Chantry (AE185.573)

John Rennie, engineer, stipple engraving, 1821, James Thomson from a bust by Sir Francis Chantry (AE185.744)

Sir James Savile, Calder Navigation, engraving, B. W. & Basire after Benjamin Wilson (AE185.574)

Sir Charles Scotter, general manager of the London & South Western Railway, a *Vanity Fair* cartoon by 'Spy', 1891 (AE185.575)

Marshall Stephens of the Manchester Ship Canal, a *Vanity Fair* cartoon by 'Elf' (AE185.576)

George Stephenson, stipple engraving, J. H. Baker after the statue by E. H. Baily (AE185.746)

George Stephenson, tinted lithograph, 1862, J. C. Lough, (design for a monument) (AE185.577)

George Stephenson, lithograph, Moses Haughton (AE185.578)

George Stephenson, mezzotint, 1849, T. L. Atkinson after John Lucas (AE185.579)

George Stephenson, mezzotint, 1838, C. Turner after H. P. Briggs (AE185.580)

Robert Stephenson, mezzotint, 1853, Samuel Bellin after John Lucas (AE185.755)

Robert Stephenson, engraving, D. J. Pound after a photograph by J. E. Mayall (AE185.581)

Robert Stephenson, mezzotint, J. R. Jackson after John Lucas (AE185.131)

Stephenson Family Group, mezzotint, 1862, Francis Holl after John Lucas (AE185.583)

Thomas Telford, mezzotint, 1831, W. Raddon after S. Lane (AE185.584)

Thomas Tredgold, engraving (AE185.585)

James Watt, stipple engraving, 1809, C. Picart after Sir William Beechey (AE185.586)

James Watt discovering the condensation of steam, mezzotint, 1869, James Scott after Marcus Stone (AE185.587)

James Watt, engraving, after a bust by Sir Francis Chantry (AE185.588)

James Watt, mezzotint, S. W. Reynolds after a bust by Sir Francis Chantry (AE185.589)

Thomas Woodhouse of the Midland Counties Railway, engraving, 1842, H. B. Hall after W. Scott (AE185.590)

# Humour and Satire

As mentioned in Chapter One, a true insight into contemporaries' feelings about their society is often best understood through the humorous drawings and prints produced at the time. From the mid-18th century onwards, a large number of satirical prints were being produced on all manner of topics ranging from the antics of royalty to the smoking habits of foreigners. Amongst these prints there was a not inconsiderable selection devoted to industry, transport and modern inventions and Elton had the opportunity to add a few choice items from these categories to his collection [**160**, **161** and **162**].

The Pleasures of the Rail-Road. – Shewing the Inconvenience of a Blow up.

**[162]**
Changing Times
Leighton Brothers patent
coloured wood engraving,
c1850
AE185.780

The artist's intentions were
obvious: the distant railway had
supplanted the road coaches
and forced the horses out to
pasture. In reality, the railways
increased the need for horses,
for shunting and for delivery
services, both by the railway
companies themselves and
by local carriers.

# Music Covers

This may seem a strange category in an industrial and transport collection, but Elton had a number of good reasons for collecting such items. Firstly, sheet music of popular tunes of the day satisfied a demand that had not existed prior to the Industrial Revolution. That demand came from a section of society that industry had helped create. What the 19th century witnessed was the emergence of an educated and image-conscious middle class. These were people who belonged to professions requiring either semi-manual or clerical skills, that had either been created by industry or new forms of transport, or if not, needed more employees as demand increased for their particular services. These new jobs required a certain education or specialist training, which also gave them a degree of status in the local community. This status was indicated with a dress code, either in the form of a uniform or a suit, by where the person lived, and by the furniture and fittings within their home. The photographs and reports of how Queen Victoria, Prince Albert and their children lived and in what domestic surroundings, greatly influenced middle class taste **[163]**. And one of the interests that the Prince Consort helped popularised was music, and the singing of songs with members of the family grouped around the piano. This instrument soon became an essential requirement for both the middle class and later the aspirational working class. In fact, so popular did the instrument become, that by 1890 there were 30 firms in Britain manufacturing pianos with an estimated combined annual output of 50,000 units. Even if only half those instruments were ever played by their owners, it indicates there was an enormous demand for sheet music.

To satisfy their audiences, librettists needed to work all manner of popular events and other shared human experiences into their work. The Great Exhibition of 1851 prompted a rash of songs, as did the International Exhibition 11 years later, shown by one example in the Elton Collection entitled, 'You had me to rights in Fifty One, but you don't in Sixty Two'. Railway themes also embraced the complete range of human emotions ripe for the song writers. There was danger — 'There's Danger on the Line' by Alfred Concanen **[164]** — or romance — 'The Charming Young Widow I met in the Train' by Alfred Concanen — or humour — 'The Muddle-Puddle Porter' by Alfred Concanen **[165]** — or drama — 'The Express Galop' by J. Brandard. The Elton Collection also contains French railway sheet music with transport themes, for

**[163]**
Farewell to the Exhibition
lithograph, 1851
J. Coventry
AE185.537

A piece of music performed on the Sommerophone in the Crystal Palace in front of Queen Victoria and Prince Albert on 14 October 1851 by the inventor, Ferdinand Sommer.

example, 'Quadrille à Vapeur', and a few American pieces that, if it were not for the colourful covers, it is difficult to believe were ever popular; the 'American Petroleum Polka' of 1864 is one of these **[166]**. In the final analysis, the illustrated covers have proved of more lasting interest than most of the 19th-century popular music they contained and, fortunately, Elton had the foresight to collect them.

[164]
The Great Semaphore Song:
There's Danger on the Line
lithograph, hand-coloured,
1875
Alfred Concanen (1835–86)
AE185.511

[165]
The Muddle-Puddle Porter
lithograph, hand-coloured,
1877
Alfred Concanen (1835–86)
published by Hopwood & Crew,
London, 16 March 1877
AE185.517

[166]
American Petroleum Polka
chromolithograph
Henry C. Eno
published by William Hall
& Son, Broadway, New
York, 1864
AE185.541

# Index

Page numbers underlined indicate illustrations and/or captions.